The Process

—*What they are saying*—

Tom's journey exploring process modeling will make BPMN even more popular. He also learns fundamentals of system analysis, business process management, relation of process modeling with IT and process model verification—often unconsciously. And Anne, his mentor, demonstrates the high value of coaching and governance in it.
—**Frank Michael Kraft**, Development Architect SAP AG, Research and Breakthrough Innovation, BPM Cluster.

Especially in economic bad times, the winning company will be the company that recognizes, understands, optimizes and reuses its business processes. Lean and green really mean something—they are dimensions of optimization for your business processes, and only those who "get it" will win. Read this book and learn.
—**Richard Soley**, Ph.D., Chairman, Object Management Group

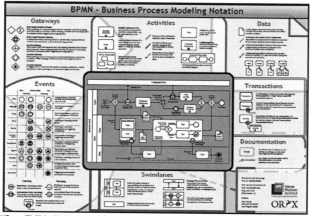

The BPMN 1.2 chart can be downloaded free from
www.bpmnbook.com
The BPMN 2.0 chart can be downloaded free from
www.bpmb.de/index.php/BPMNPoster

Publisher's Cataloging-in-Publication Data

Grosskopf, Alexander.
The Process: Business Process Modeling Using BPMN / Alexander Grosskopf,
Gero Decker, Mathias Weske.
1st ed.
    p. cm.
Includes bibliographical references and index.
ISBN-10: 0-929652-26-6   ISBN-13: 978-0-929652-26-9
1. Business Process Management 2. Process Modeling. 3. Notation Standard.
4. Process Analysis. 5. Organizational change. I. Grosskopf, Alexander. II. Title

HM48.G75 2006   Librrary of Congress No. 2009923535
303.48'33–dc22   CIP

Published by Meghan-Kiffer Press
310 East Fern Street — Suite G
Tampa, FL 33604 USA

Company and product names mentioned herein are the trademarks or registered
trademarks of their respective owners.

Meghan-Kiffer books are available at special quantity discounts for corporate educa-
tion and training use. For more information write Special Sales, Meghan-Kiffer
Press, Suite G, 310 East Fern Street, Tampa, Florida 33604 or email
info@mkpress.com

Meghan-Kiffer Press, USA

Printed in the United States of America.   SAN 249-7980
MK Printing 10 9 8 7 6 5 4 3 2

THE PROCESS

BUSINESS PROCESS MODELING USING BPMN

Alexander Grosskopf, Gero Decker, Mathias Weske

Meghan-Kiffer Press
Tampa, Florida, USA, www.mkpress.com
Innovation at the Intersection of Business and Technology

Table of Contents

Acknowledgements

The challenges of Dr. Ingo Decker inspired us to write this book about process modeling along the use cases of a medium-sized high-tech company. Thanks to his experience as a CEO and founder of several laser companies we learned about the domain and the needs from a management perspective. One of his companies served as role model for LaserTec, the scene for this book. All the names used in the book are fictional. Similarities to existing people or companies are a coincidence.

We also thank Daniela Weske for hand-drawing Anne's process models. Her contribution made the book livelier and more authentic. Finally, we thank our friends, colleagues and the professional reviewers for their valuable feedback. A great big thanks also to Scottie Jacob from Meghan-Kiffer Press for her professional assistance.

Chapter 1

The New Assistant

He wiped off his sweaty hand before pressing down the door handle.

"Hello, my name is Tom Bauer," he said while standing in the door. He felt his heart beating as he took his first step into the room. The office was large, and the furniture was in the style of the mid 90s. The man behind the desk had not yet laid an eye on Tom. He seemed to be concentrating on something else. The desktop was cluttered with piles of documents, books, and loose sheets of paper. The creative chaos of a working man, Tom thought as he came to the front of the desk.

"Hello, Mr. Bauer!" the man said, and in the same moment stood up, reached out his hand, over the large desk, and focused on Tom's eyes. "Hello, Mr. Haffner," Tom answered.

"Please, take a seat." Haffner picked up a clean cup from a side table, held it toward Tom and asked, "May I offer you coffee, Mr. Bauer?"

"No, thank you," Tom answered. Haffner poured coffee into his cup while Tom settled into his chair. "Yeah, well, the job," Haffner started after a few minutes of small talk. "Let's see. 'Associate executive,' that's the title we chose for the position." Haffner picked up a loose sheet of paper from the side of his desk. Tom recognized the curriculum vitae he had sent along with his job application.

"Mr. Bauer, I have invited you because here it says you have expertise in organizational management and controlling. Do you?"

"Yes Sir, I've been best in class and received my degree with honors," Tom answered confidently.

"From your profile you seem to fit to the job." Haffner started again. He leaned back, took a sip of coffee and explained, "When I bought this company fourteen years ago I had thirteen employees, and I knew them all personally. I mean, not only their names, but their hobbies and family situations as well. We were supplying laser components for five large customers. Do you know how many customers LaserTec has as of today?"

"About three hundred spread all over the world," Tom quickly responded.

Haffner recognized that this young man had done his homework. He turned his chair toward the window, looked down at the factory premises, and said, "With every year, our products have evolved. With every job we took on, we needed to hire more people, and the company changed and grew in complexity."

After a short pause, Haffner continued, "Our core business involves world class laser units. We supply them directly to customers and also to production line manufactures, for instance, in the car industry. Then, we have our after-sales services, such as maintenance, availability promises, and laser refurbishment. On top of all that we also have the in-house job of order production which we do to fill up idle capacity."

Haffner started a monologue about the priorities of primary and secondary business. Tom tried to follow the storyline. He nodded his head to affirm his attention, but Haffner didn't see it. "Three years ago one of our suppliers for lenses went bankrupt. Can you believe that? He just went out of business – no more lenses! Our customers couldn't care less; they wanted their devices! Of course, over the years we looked at several suppliers, but these guys had the best material." Tom nodded, and thought about the supply chain lectures at the university, while Haffner continued.

"Anyway, we needed a solution, and quickly. But there was no supplier on the horizon to deliver the quality and know-how needed for our systems. So I went to the supplier and negotiated the buy-out of the lenses development and production. It didn't look too bad until the next day, when I realized that the employees were not willing to move four hundred kilometers to the north in order to join our team. To solve that, I had to keep the supplier's existing location, letting the employees stay in their homes with their families. This all happened within forty-eight hours."

Haffner emptied his coffee cup and refilled it. He looked at Tom who didn't know what to say.

"Was it a good decision? Yes. Did I know it back then? No. Two weeks later we got an engineer-to-order request for a very strong laser unit. Something we hadn't done before. We needed new optical parts as well. The people in our newly founded R&D department were excited and worked really hard to get the job done. Now we have the best optical parts for all our lasers at hand."

Haffner leaned back. He appeared to be exhausted by the monologue. A short smile flashed on his face. Tom liked the story but couldn't see how he would fit into the scene.

"What do you think my contribution to LaserTec could be?" Tom asked.

"You see, it is my job to steer the ship. I do that by making decisions. With better insights about our work I can make better decisions. But there is much about this company that I don't know – not anymore."

Tom felt that Haffner was coming to the point. "You see, with every new employee things have shifted a bit. Over the years I lost track of the changes. And now I cannot just step on anyone's door and ask questions about their work. Besides, I have other things to do. And here is where you come into the game. I want you to deeply understand how we work, the underlying processes. And I want you to get me the numbers. I have already made too many decisions without accurate consideration of the processes and without a sound quantitative basis. Some people call this kind of job a process analyst, or, for the quantitative part, a controller. I would rather say that you would be my eyes and ears! "

Mr. Haffner paused for a moment and looked at Tom. Then he continued, "I have a good feeling about you, Mr. Bauer. I want you on board!"

Tom was a little bit puzzled. This all still sounded a bit too unspecific. "So what would I do exactly?"

"Well, I recently met an old friend who also owns a mid-sized company, like LaserTec," Haffner replied, "and we talked a lot about how to view our businesses. What perspective to take. He told me that he is into a process-oriented point of view, seeing everything from end to end. Always having in mind what steps really create the value and who is involved in the process. What information is needed when and where handovers take too much time. Always caring about how to improve, where to increase quality, reduce waste or save time. I would like you to take on that perspective. Get the process skills, become our process expert. You have a fresh view, straight from the university, full of ideas! "

Tom thought about this for a few moments. "But isn't there anybody with that kind of expertise in your company already?"

"Good question," Haffner replied. "Mrs. White. She has some experience in the process field. In her previous job she did quite a bit of process modeling. Somehow I didn't realize the value of that knowledge up until now. When she joined us I put her in charge of organizing the order processing. That totally ate up her time. And now it's already too late..."

"Too late?"

"Unfortunately, Mrs. White is leaving the company," Haffner answered with a sad voice. "She reduced herself to a half-time position already. And in less than six months she will be gone completely. So it's high time she passes on her experience. I think you will get along with her." After a short pause he continued, "Oh, sorry – I don't want to rush you into anything. Take your time to think about the offer. After all, it's an important decision!"

Tom repeated the comment in his head. It is indeed an important decision. Becoming the process expert of LaserTec and directly working for the CEO? This could be the beginning of a very exciting time.

Chapter 2

All Models are Incomplete

Tom leaned back in the comfortable arm chair. His weekend was exhausting. The day he returned the signed contract, he also decided to rent a two-bedroom apartment at the center of LaserTec's small town.

He would have enough time to talk to everyone involved in order to get to know how the company worked and what to do. So for now he could enjoy the view of the factory premises, where some workers were piling up steel plates at the factory building. Tom heard the workers saying that the boss wanted the steel plates to be cut and sent back by the end of the week. Next week a new project would start, with the pre-assembly and testing of a new laser unit. Tom thought back to what Haffner had said about peripheral business and core business. Laser engineering is the core business, and this new order would probably require the company's full attention.

The door opened, and a middle-aged lady bolted in. "You must be Tom, right?" she asked, while starting the coffee machine with a few rehearsed steps.

She reached out her hand. Tom noticed her friendly eyes and warm manner. "My name is Anne, Anne White," she said.

"A pleasure to meet you, Mrs. White."

"Please, call me Anne."

Anne took a seat in the armchair where Tom was sitting before she arrived. She turned on her computer and grabbed three sheets of paper from the fax machine without even looking. The faxes from last night, he thought. She glanced at them and put them on a pile of other faxes. The faxes on the pile were all post-it-strewn and super-scripted with annotations.

Anne started the conversation, "Mr. Haffner already told me that somebody is finally taking on the process perspective in this company. That's an excellent idea. I tried to convince him several times. But finally he started thinking about it – only because his old buddy suddenly told him some fantastic stories."

Anne scanned through one of the three pages she held in her hand. She continued, "Let's not waste time; let's get right into it. Ready for the processes?"

"Sure!" Tom couldn't wait to start.

Anne began her monologue, "There is a very important thing you have to know right from the start. If you want to be the master of your processes, you have to know them first. And it is not sufficient that a single person knows them. You have to get a shared under-standing of what you are talking about. Unfortunately, processes are somehow invisible. It's not like a house that you build, and where you can see where each room is located. Or where you can see how the roof collapses if it is not properly designed. Processes are somehow intangible. But they do exist. Therefore, the main challenge is to visu-alize them. To nail them down on paper. Only then can you discuss them and point to parts you are most interested in."

Anne took a deep breath and then continued, "Process modeling is at the very heart of the company. It is about understanding how the company operates – giving names to things that happen. It is about observing, and it's about writing it all down. But enough with the general stuff. Let's get directly into our processes. That'll make things clearer."

"Good idea," Tom thought, as he watched her grab a blank sheet of paper.

"Let's start off with the big picture," she started. "In essence, we are developing and selling laser devices. We are not the biggest player around, but we have quite a good reputation for creating tricky custom solutions. Do you happen to have any background in engineering?"

"I'm afraid, I haven't," Tom said.

"Not a problem," Anne reassured him, "I'm not an engineer either. You know, sometimes I have the feeling that without outsiders like us this company would end up in chaos," she said jokingly. "But you should definitely have a basic understanding of what lasers are good for. Any ideas?"

Tom thought for a minute before replying. The first thing that came to his mind was Luke Skywalker's laser sword, but he managed to suppress his smile. "Isn't it all about precision?" Tom finally suggested.

"That's true. Precision is our business," Anne said, "With lasers you can cut any kind of material with maximum precision. Any kind of metal, plastic, glass, even wood. And lasers are just taking off. We are expanding every year to keep up with the customers' requirements," Anne continued. "It even surprises me from time to time what our customers actually use these machines for."

Then she stopped and quickly scanned through the faxes. She

picked out one with a purple post-it on it.

"Take this customer for instance," Anne held up the fax. "We developed lasers for printing their company logo onto heat insulation plates. Much more efficient than the burning technique they used before."

"Sounds like LaserTec has a lot of innovative ideas."

"Indeed," Anne replied, "But great ideas and innovative products are only one side of the coin. With the number of people involved, somebody has to organize the work. Unfortunately, people tend to see only their particular function in the system."

"You mean they are not aware of the context of their work?" Tom tried to rephrase Anne's statement.

"That's my point! It's about coordinating the work that all employees do, so that the right hand knows what the left hand is doing, how work is handed over. Did you know that almost everybody in the company is involved on the path from the customer request to the installation at the customer's site?"

Anne started drawing. Several boxes appeared in a row. Tom leaned over to get a better view.

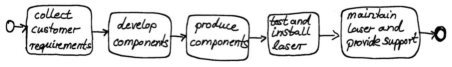

"I like to put things visually, you know, and that is already a key ingredient of process modeling – visual representation," Anne went on while filling text into the drawing. "Here are the most important steps we are doing."

Tom started reading. The five steps looked somewhat familiar to him. "First of all, our project engineers need to identify what the customer wants," Anne explained, "I call this 'collect customer requirements,' here," she said while pointing at the first box. "Then our engineers develop the components. Especially in difficult cases, this can take up to two months. Once we are done with that, production starts."

"Production means that you build the laser in that step?" Tom asked, to keep up.

"Well, the laser unit is typically a larger machine. It has the optical components to create the stream of light but also a frame and the mechanical parts to get material in and out of the machine. All these parts are specified in this step here," Anne pointed at the rectangle named 'develop components,' and they are then created in the production step."

"I see," Tom replied, although he didn't yet imagine how this would look in reality.

"The final step before a laser becomes operational is the testing and installation phase. As almost every machine is a custom development, this phase needs special attention."

"Finally, maintenance and support. Of course, that's needed as well," Tom concluded.

"And guess what is special about the last phase?" Anne challenged him.

As Tom didn't know where Anne was heading, she proceeded, "That's where we make our money. Support gives us the actual margins. Just selling the machines wouldn't be enough."

Anne looked straight at him, "What you see here in the diagram are only the basics. Once you move into more detail it gets far more tricky and complex."

"I like your drawing," Tom said.

"I'm happy you like it. But hey, it's more than a drawing. It's a model. A process model."

"Drawing. Model. Where is the difference?" Tom asked.

"All these elements here have a well defined meaning. I don't make them up. They are a standardized way to write things down," Anne continued, "That's what distinguishes a model from a drawing."

"I see. But to me the meaning is intuitive," he pointed at Anne's drawing, "I mean, everybody would understand it. Why not allow everybody to draw the way he or she likes it?"

"What would you draw differently? Give me an example," Anne said in reply.

"What about using icons, such as a question mark, to represent testing?"

"Ok, let's assume question marks were scattered all over the model," Anne retorted. "How should I interpret them? That there are decisions to be made? That some parts need clarification? Or that you are not sure about the process?"

Tom laughed out loud.

Anne smiled and continued, "Processes can get quite complex. They are not always as simple as the five step process you just saw."

"You mean with many more boxes?" Tom threw in.

"It is not only that," Anne responded. "You might want to incorporate rich knowledge about the routing order of activities, the people involved, or the information needed."

Tom said reflectively, "So there are more things to draw than boxes, arrows, and circles?"

"Absolutely! There are variations of these symbols, but there are also others," Anne responded.

"And you are going to teach me all this?" Tom asked.

He looked into her eyes. She looked back and smiled.

"I already have so many ideas about how to extend this," Tom added, "what to add to the model."

Anne looked at him and said in a strict tone of voice, "Again, stick to the standards! Believe me, a lot of stuff is already covered. Just imagine you make up your own symbols. It would end up in a Babylonian clutter of languages nobody would understand. Process models are visual artifacts to communicate content."

Tom agreed with her explanation. Anne went on, "We need a common understanding of what the symbols mean; we need common semantics. The languages of these drawings are called process-modeling languages. Have you come across any of those already?"

He once started a course at the university but liked neither the professor nor the students attending the class. So he simply dropped out. "How shall I say...?" he started.

"Okay, so you have no experience," she said. "Coffee?"

Anne jumped up, briefly sniffed the coffee and started pouring it into the cups. Tom thanked her as she handed over a cup to him. He didn't like coffee too much but didn't feel like saying so. Anne obviously loved coffee.

"Take your seat over here," she said. "Let's have a look at a particular process. Let's dispatch customer requests."

She grabbed another sheet of paper with a green post-it on it from the stack of faxes on her desk.

"Aha," she said while scanning the first fax message. "So, this seems to be a new customer."

She started diving into the file structures on her computer. Eventually, she opened a spreadsheet and searched it for the name denoted in the header of the message. No result.

"Okay, since this is a new customer to us, we create what we call a sales opportunity."

Anne opened another spreadsheet and filled in the information from the fax message. Tom leaned over to get a better view on her computer screen. Within a few moments Anne had created a new customer profile and filled in the data from the fax.

"To dispatch the request we have to send an email to the pre-sales people. This triggers them to take a look at the spreadsheet and contact the potential customer," Anne said while proceeding. "The spreadsheet file is stored on a network drive, so that they can access it," she explained.

She sent the email, closed the spreadsheet, and turned to Tom. "That's it for dispatching requests. Any questions?"

Tom looked at her, puzzled. Can that be the whole customer request dispatching process?

"What about existing customers?" he asked.

"Good question!" Anne took a sip of coffee and proceeded, "For each customer who already has a laser from LaserTec, we have a dedicated sales accountant. Typically the one who had the last contact with the customer."

She spoke about the strategy for customer satisfaction and that LaserTec had three hundred customers all over the world – each of them deserving particular treatment. As she continued talking, Tom's attention was fading away. The stories from customers in Arabia and Asia with their cultural backgrounds inspired his thoughts. One day he might be traveling around the world to meet all these customers, have a beer in Vancouver or a Mango Lassi in Delhi.

Anne looked at him for a moment to get his full attention before she continued. "Maybe, it's time to pinpoint this process on paper."

She took a blank sheet of paper from the printer and started to draw with a pencil. Tom watched her, while circles, rectangles, and diamond shaped elements appeared on the paper. It didn't seem to make any sense in the beginning. As she started adding phrases to the diagram, he could link some of them back to the story she had told.

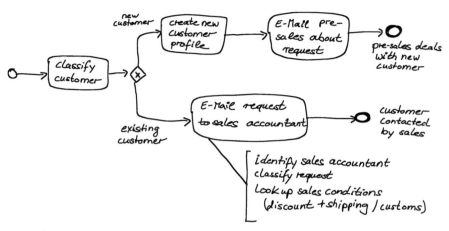

Shortly afterward, she put the pencil aside and shoved the paper toward him. Tom read the phrases in the diagram. Then he pointed at a rectangle that said "email request to sales accountant."

"How do you know which sales accountant to contact for a particular customer?" he asked.

"Oh, yes, I forgot," Anne responded and put additional text at the side of the diagram. "We can identify the sales person from the spreadsheet you saw initially," Anne said. "While we are there it is also a good idea to look up the sales conditions for the particular type of request."

Tom nodded, "I see."

"We have many different customers all over the world, and each one has an individual contract that defines all sorts of details; for instance, the discounts for spare parts or component upgrades. In addition, each country has special conditions for customs, which is also important information we must incorporate."

Tom turned his attention to the model on the sheet of paper. The shapes were new to him, but, from the context, he thought he was able to give it meaning.

"Is this now a business process language?" he asked.

"This," Anne pointed at the sketch, "is a business process diagram. The language is called BPMN."

"BPMN?" Tom responded without thinking.

Anne explained, "BPMN stands for Business Process Modeling Notation. It is the state-of-the-art in process modeling."

"Okay, so how do you read this diagram?"

"That's simple."

Anne leaned back in her chair while Tom bent over the paper with the sketchy drawing.

"It always starts with a circle," Anne continued, pointing her pencil to the details of the drawing. "The arrows indicate the order in which things are done."

"So the first thing is to classify the customer," Tom explained to get more confidence.

"Exactly."

"What do you call these shapes?" Tom asked.

"The initial circle is called start event, the arrows are called sequence flows, and the rectangle with the rounded edge is an activity."

"Too easy," said Tom and stretched his legs. "Let me guess, the diamond shape with the cross in the middle is a decision."

"Correct," Anne responded. "It's called a data-based exclusive gateway. I usually say XOR gateway. Here, one of the outgoing branches is taken."

Tom read through the diagram again, "And the circles with the thicker line?"

"End events," Anne immediately responded, "They indicate the end of the process."

Tom nodded his head. It all sounded intuitive. But somehow he had the feeling that this cannot be all there is to it. He pointed at the text at the side of the drawing.

"Has this a particular meaning as well?" he asked.

"Yes, it means that I should rework the process," she joked with some irony. "It is called annotation. It's basically free text without a formal meaning, but you can annotate and comment on everything with it. In BPMN it is part of the language," Anne started loading a program on her computer.

"Annotations are a useful tool for adding arbitrary documentation to a process model. But here, we better refine the process model to put in that information."

Anne turned toward the computer and the program that she had just started. It has a set of drawing elements similar to those on the paper, but a lot more. Tom observed her intently, while she was arranging the modeling elements on a canvas. Once the process was recreated, she saved the file and started talking while she edited the model on the screen.

"First of all, this process is started by new requests from customers. They typically come in by email or fax." She changed the start event against a similar looking shape, which contained a letter icon inside the circle.

"I see icons. There are many different icons," Tom remarked.

"Yes, there is a defined set of symbols in BPMN. Like the letter symbol which indicates that a message is received."

"I see, and receiving the message is what starts the process?"

"Correct."

"So, the other model was incorrect?" Tom asked.

"I'd prefer to call it 'less accurate'," Anne replied, "The information about what starts the process was simply not given in the previous process model."

After Anne added the phrase "customer request by fax or email" to the start event, she went on and changed the process part for the existing customers.

"I classify the customer request and identify the sales conditions for a customer," Anne explained. "After that, I identify the sales representative from the spreadsheet, as you just saw. After this is done I send the email to the sales representative."

"Why do you have to classify the request?" Tom looked at Anne waiting for a reaction. "Oh," Anne said, "existing customers typically ask for either spare parts to put on stock or they want to upgrade certain components." Anne added an annotation to the activity. "Upgrades and spare parts have different discounts for each customer," she explained. "Also, we have special shipping restrictions related to customs for each part of the world, sometimes even per country."

"I see," Tom said, and this time he really felt that he had under-stood something.

He reached for the mouse, which Anne willingly gave to him. From the set of model elements he dragged another annotation to the canvas. He connected it to the activity "Identify sales conditions" and filled in some text. He pressed the "Save" button, leaned back, and looked at the result with contended feelings. Anne smiled at him.

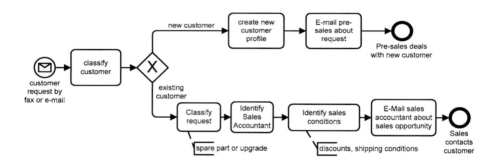

"So, for existing customers," he started thinking aloud, "you first classify the request and then you can look up the sales accountant and the sales conditions."

"Yes, and if I have gathered this information I can send out the email to the sales accountant," Anne continued, "so that they can contact the customer."

"And after that there is nothing more for you to do?"

"That's it, the process ends for me there. That's my perspective on it. Sales is then in charge for all further contacts to this customer."

Tom nodded, "But I thought that process modeling is about bridging activities – seeing it as a whole?"

"You are absolutely right," Anne replied. "That is a core part of understanding processes. If the hand-over between the different activities does not work properly, if the different people involved don't collaborate properly, the overall process will be far from optimal. But, you know, I am not really an expert in sales. I am working in the product management division. I am afraid you'll need to talk to someone from that division to learn more about the overall process."

Anne printed the process model. Tom took the sheet of paper from the printer and wandered around in Anne's office. He concentrated on the model, going through each step again.

"It might be," Anne interrupted, "that we get a refurbishment request for a used laser unit. Um...," she quickly scanned the faxes. "None here. They are rare, but they do happen."

"How would you handle a refurbishment request?" Tom asked.

"We know quite a lot about the laser units installed at our customers' organizations. All information about a laser unit is kept in a particular folder in our network file system."

Tom looked up at Anne and instantly recognized that there was obviously another branch in the process that they have not yet talked about.

"What information do you store?"

"Almost everything – you name it. The product engineering documents specify which components they have used, when and where these components have been produced, and all the history of the initial project, starting with the specification and ending with the installation report. Also, there are the maintenance reports for the laser unit. It's important, you know. When we refurbish, we need to know in advance what's coming."

Tom grabbed a pen and started noting down something on the sheet of paper with the printed model.

"And how do you handle these requests?"

"Come here and I'll show you," Anne said and turned toward her computer screen. Tom walked over to Anne and sat down on the chair next to her. Anne browsed through the file structures again and ended up with a folder with many, many other folders in it. Anne went into one of the folders and explained the folder's structure. Everything was named systematically. "With a few clicks, I can find all the information I need," she explained.

"What happens if you get ill?" Tom asked.

Anne gave Tom a blank stare, "Everybody else has access to these folders." Tom wasn't sure whether anybody at LaserTec would find the required information in the folder structure. "I think we should put it here," Anne reopened the modeling program and started changing the process model. "Refurbishment requests can only come from existing customers. But we should then classify the requests to distinguish spare parts and upgrade requests from refurbishment requests."

"So this is another decision then," Tom said while trying to follow Anne's explanation.

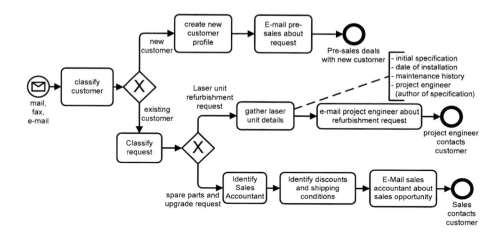

"Correct." She took another XOR gateway and placed it in the active diagram.

Tom watched her silently while she changed the process model. Afterward, he took the mouse and pointed at the newly introduced activity with the name "gather laser unit details."

"So what is the information you gather at that point?"

"We need to, at least, extract the initial specification, the date of installation, and the maintenance history."

Tom took an annotation shape from the BPMN element selection, put it on the canvas, and connected it with the activity. He filled in the comments by Anne and then proceeded along the execution path.

"If you go along this branch," he followed the branch for a refurbishment request, "how do you identify which project engineer to contact? There is no activity for that."

"That is correct. There could be another activity to do that. Actually, the project engineer to contact is the one responsible for the initial specification. Therefore, I simply open the specification file and have a look at the author."

Tom extended the annotation he just added with the information about the project engineer. He saved the model, hit the print button, and went over to the printer.

"I like this process language," he said.

"Not my invention, but very useful," Anne retorted.

"Is the model I have here showing completely what you do?"

"Oh dear," Anne laughed, "All models are incomplete. It's the nature of a model to reflect aspects of the reality. A subset. They can never be complete. But if this subset helps to understand what is done then the model is useful."

Tom smiled at her, while she turned back to her screen. He took out his small black book and a pen. He opened the first page. The book was blank, no words yet. He looked at Anne who was working on her computer without paying attention to him. When he turned back to the first empty page in his little black book he started noting down.

All models are incomplete; some are useful.

He flipped the first page of the note book and redrew the shapes from the BPMN diagram. With the printed process model on his knees, he noted down the semantics of the elements as he recalled it.

The office turned silent. For almost ten minutes nobody talked. Only the sound of Anne typing with moderate speed on her computer could be heard.

"These gateways," Tom broke the silence, "you use them to open up alternative branches?"

Anne took her hands off the keyboard and looked at Tom.

"But what if...." He was staring at Anne, but he seemed to look through her.

"But what if, what?" Anne echoed impatiently.

"I was just thinking of a situation, where you do alternative things," he started explaining, "but later on, you need to do the same thing anyway. You know what I mean?"

"You mean," Anne picked up the ball, "if you do different things for different customers but in the end reply to the customer anyway."

"Yes, exactly," Tom blurted out.

"Not a problem at all." She sketched something on a sheet of paper. While Tom stared at the paper, Anne explained, "You can use the same gateway for that because it has split and merge semantics."

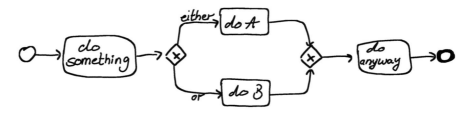

As Tom didn't react, Anne continued, "Look at the drawing. You can split the process flow to alternative branches. So, you either do A or you do B. If you also want to bring these alternative branches back together, you can join them by using the XOR gateway."

Tom inspected the sketch on the sheet of paper.

"If they can be used for both," Tom asked, "can there be multiple incoming and outgoing sequence flows for the same gateway?"

"Yes. You can use the same gateway for merging and splitting the process flow at the same time. But I would suggest to do it in two separate gateways." Anne remembered the lengthy discussions she had with her old colleagues about different modeling styles.

"It is always a good idea to keep the models simple. If you overload a construct with too many semantics, people get confused. Process modeling is not about showing that you can use the fanciest constructs. It is about sharing knowledge. Only when everybody understands the model in the same way, can you gain something from it."

"So semantics are all about an agreed understanding," Tom said absently. "I will have to talk to a lot of people to get all the different perspectives on it."

"Exactly," Anne answered. "That is actually a very good idea. As a next step, you should meet somebody from production to learn more about what they do. That will help you gather more parts of the puzzle."

Tom was busy noting down comments in his little black book. Anne turned toward the clock over the door to her office. It was already noon.

"Oh, time for lunch!" She immediately jumped up and grabbed her purse. Standing in the door she turned back to Tom. "Let's go! "

Plain Start Event
Is the starting point of the process. A plain start event leaves open what actually starts the process.

Start Message Event
Arrival of a message starts the process. This can be either via fax, mail, email, or any other message-like communication.

Plain End Event
Denotes the end of an execution path for the process.

Activity
Is a unit of work. Something to be done. Something that takes time. Activities in BPMN are called Tasks if they cannot be decomposed.

Sequence Flow
Describes the order in which things are done. It can connect events, activities, and gateways.

XOR Gateway
Used to split or join the sequence flow. When splitting the flow, one of the outgoing branches is taken. When joining the process flow it merges every incoming branch into the outgoing branch.

Textual Annotation
Free textual description. Can be attached to everything to give further explanations. Has no process semantics but is free text.

Chapter 3

It's all about People

The next morning Tom decided to walk to the office. The way to LaserTec led through a small park and ended in an industrial area. LaserTec was located at the heart of this area, along with other companies dealing with logistics and car accessories.

Tom needed to find Arthur Winning to learn more about production at LaserTec. Anne had told him that he spent most of the time in the factory building across from the office building. A yard as big as a football field was in between both. The yard was filled with containers as tall as men. Just before entering the factory building, he saw Winning with a group of men in front of a container. They were talking and laughing. Tom walked toward them. Winning saw Tom approaching and stepped aside from the group.

"May I have some of your time, Sir," Tom said to Winning, while he was still five meters away.

"Hello, Mr. Bauer," Winning replied as they shook hands. "Mr. Haffner told me about you. I am sorry but I only have little time. What's the matter?"

Tom replied, "I need to know more about the development process at LaserTec, and I assume you are the best source of information for that."

"You bet I am," Winning replied. "You can join me for a short walk if you like, and we can use the time to talk."

"That would be great, thanks."

Winning took a sheet of paper. They started walking around in the labyrinth of containers. Winning compared the numbers on the containers with those listed on his sheet of paper.

"This week we have started a new project. The guys over there," Winning pointed at the group of men still standing and talking, "are the project engineers. These people are specialists in electronics, optical engineering, and precision mechanics. Laser development is not a standard procedure, you know. At least not for the kind of lasers we produce here. We have done dozens of projects and yet every project is different."

After a short pause, Winning continued, "This project will keep us busy for weeks. And at this very moment, we are about to have the kick-off session."

"Kick-off session?" Tom asked.

"In the beginning we agree on a general idea on how the laser unit should be constructed. Kind of an initial specification of the laser. This is an important step, because from there on we can start developing the individual components. This has to happen by tomorrow. After that, all these guys can work on their own and develop the components needed for the laser."

"I see," Tom said to keep Winning going, "and what happens then?"

"Sorry, I am really short of time. I have to go to the team meeting just now."

"May I join?" Tom was eager to get involved.

"It's about the laser unit specification, but, sure, you're welcome, of course."

They went over to the group of men. Tom was briefly introduced to them before the group moved on to the factory floor. Tom was amazed to see that the factory building was just a big hall with two large machines. One machine was working and spitting out cylinders into a basket. Three men with blue overalls inspected the resulting cylinders. They stopped the machine, then everybody fiddled about with something, and then they started the machine again. It was a fascinating display that attracted Tom's attention.

The meeting went on for an hour. When a delivery boy from a catering service brought in sandwiches, Winning allowed a twenty-minute break. Still, everybody was using the break for discussions about the new laser unit.

"See, that's the way we do it," Winning addressed Tom, who was busy with his sandwich. "Sometimes we have more time, so we split up the kick-off meeting to two days. But it's good to discuss everything through once before we start."

"Start what?" Tom asked.

"The development part," Winning responded. "All we discuss here are the initial ideas and the work distribution. Later on, everybody works on his own, more or less independently."

"More or less?"

"The optical guys work together, and the mechanical guys and so on. But apart from that, development can happen independently."

"What happens after you finish your development?"

"We move on to the next project. There is always work to do." Winning finally decided to grab one of the remaining sandwiches.

"But how does the project continue?" Tom continued asking.

"The guys from technical services take over." Winning pointed at the other side of the factory floor. The three men dressed in blue were still tinkering with their machine. "We specify, and they build the components needed."

"And then?"

"The standard stuff; they have to assemble the parts to a laser unit. Then they test and configure it. You see," he pointed over to the men at the other side. "They have been configuring and fine-tuning this machine for weeks now."

Winning clapped his hands, and the meeting resumed. Tom stayed in the meeting for another hour. He couldn't follow the details of the technical discussions, but enjoyed the engineering spirit. After the meeting Tom went to Winning to ask him more questions.

"So, did you learn anything, Mr. Bauer?" Winning asked. "Quite technical, huh?"

"That's true. I still got quite a bit of information. But I have some more questions I'd like to ask you."

Winning took a look at his watch for the first time since the meeting started. "Sure. But please, keep it short." He started walking toward the exit of the factory building.

"How do you proceed until the laser finally operates at the customer site?" Tom wanted to know.

"What you saw here was project engineering. It includes the planning and component development. After that the assembly and testing starts."

"Who produces the components?"

"Oh, usually we do it; the guys over there." He pointed at the men dressed in blue. "The technical services group, just like project engineering, is a part of product management, and that's me. We produce, assemble, configure, and test the lasers. In the end, we also package, ship, and install them at the customer's site."

"Why do you test the laser units here?"

Winning stopped, turned toward Tom, and lectured him. "Mr. Bauer, the laser units produced here need extensive testing. They are high-tech devices that are highly customized. We can't afford problems at the customer site. Here at LaserTec we have all the expertise at hand. Can you imagine what it costs to do three weeks of testing in Japan?"

"Um, makes sense now that I think about it," Tom admitted. As they reached the yard in front of the factory building, Winning asked "Anything more that I can do for you, Mr. Bauer?"

"No, I don't want to hold you back. Just one more question," Tom said. "Who carries out the work in Japan?"

"Our own people," Winning said. "My people from the technical services team go East and install the machines they have built and tested here. In the end, I am liable for everything. That's why I always inspect the final handover certificate signed by the customer. You never know."

"I see," Tom said.

"I really have to leave now." Winning turned his back toward Tom to leave. After a few steps he stopped and turned back to Tom, "Good luck with your work, Mr. Bauer."

When Tom returned to his office, he knew that he had enough information to model a process. However, it still wasn't easy. For another hour he itemized details from the project engineering meeting on a sheet of paper. Yet he couldn't see how all this activity could result in a process model. Due to the long meeting, his concentration suffered. Finally, he sketched a diagram that, in his opinion, reflected his understanding of the process as accurately as he could.

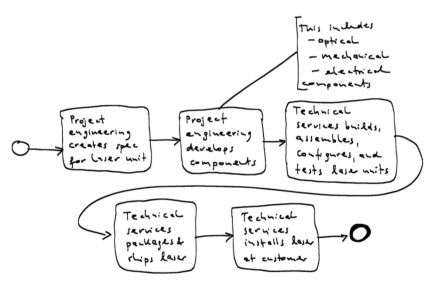

When Tom reviewed the process in the afternoon, his dissatisfaction grew. He felt that there must be more expressiveness in modeling the situation. He would need more help with that. He decided to ask Anne.

42

"Hi, Tom. How are you? Coffee?" Anne was all smiles again.

She jumped up from her chair and went over to the coffee machine. Without hesitating or waiting for Tom's answer, she poured a cup for him.

"Anne, I modeled the first stuff on my own," he waved the paper with the handwritten process model, "and I thought you might be interested."

"Sure I am. Show it to me!" Anne grabbed the paper out of Tom's hand and looked at it. "Um... so you already talked to Winning, uh-huh ...." Thoughtfully, Anne inspected the model. She flipped the page, then flipped it back. She took it to her chair and sat down.

"Is that all?" Anne asked. "Is that the whole process? Five activities in a sequence?"

"Well, the process, of course, is more complex, but I didn't know how to express that," Tom admitted.

"Why did you write down 'project engineering' and 'technical services' all the time?" Anne asked.

"See what I mean?" Tom replied, "I did not know how to express that this process is done by different people with different qualifications."

"Ah, I see. You need a role concept," Anne said.

Tom didn't understand.

"A role concept allows you to express who performs a task. I'll show you." Anne turned toward her computer. Within a minute, Anne redrew the diagram from Tom's hand drawing.

"I like to keep models digital," Anne explained, "so you can easily change and version them."

"I need this program," Tom said. "Where can I get it?"

"I'll send you the link to the Web site where you can find it," Anne responded. "You don't even need to install anything on your computer. It's a Web-based thing." Anne saved the process model and then started changing it. She dragged a big rectangle shape from the shape repository and dropped it onto the canvas.

"So this is LaserTec," she said. "And the people involved in that process are the technical services guys and the project engineers. Right?"

"Yes, they hand the work over after the specification is done," Tom said.

"BPMN allows you to express the process ownership using a pool."

"Pool?" Tom raised his eyebrows.

"Yes, like a swimming pool. That's actually where the metaphor comes from." Anne said and smiled, "BPMN makes use of 'swim-lanes' as a concept to organize activities into separate visual areas. Each swimlane illustrates different functional capabilities or responsibilities. In BPMN the swimlane idea is mapped to 'pools' and 'lanes.'"

Tom frowned to indicate his lack of understanding. Anne pointed at the left border of the large rectangle where she had already written down the name "LaserTec."

"A pool represents an organization. Processes are run by organizations. You can represent that a process is run by a particular organization by creating a pool and placing the process inside." Anne went on and created smaller rectangles dividing the pool into multiple nested rectangles.

She put the names "Project Engineering" and "Technical Services" into the head of the new rectangles. Afterwards, Anne dragged the process model into the pool and started rearranging the activities inside.

"Because an organization is usually more complex, you can sub-divide the pool into lanes, each representing a sub-division of the organization. Now you can place each activity in the lane that corresponds to the role that actually performs the work."

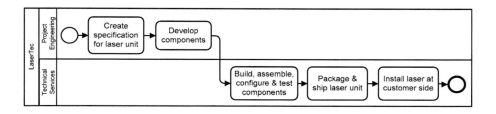

"That's exactly what I needed," Tom said. "Now we have only two roles here. I guess I can have as many lanes in a pool as I like?"

"You can even sub-divide lanes," Anne said. "So you can dive arbitrarily deep into the structure of the organization."

"Even down to individuals," Tom tried to conclude Anne's remarks.

"Well, it's more about roles, right? You could name an individual person, but you'd normally rather stick to the role which the person performs in the given context."

"Why not directly name the person?" Tom was curious. "Why is this role concept so important?"

"Of course, you could put the name of a particular person in there," Anne started explaining, "but typically you have several people that fulfill the same role. One person might also have different roles in different contexts. The role reflects qualifications and responsibilities. It's just a useful level of abstraction on top of individual people."

"I see." Tom compared the process model on the screen with his hand-drawn model. "There is something else that I could not express." He pointed at the annotation in his drawing. "See, the project engineers are splitting up to develop the optical, the mechanical, and the electrical parts. What I'd like to express is that these people work independently."

"In parallel, so to say," Anne picked up his thoughts.

"Exactly. They do an initial specification together, but then they split up in three teams, each working on their parts."

"There are ways to express parallelism in BPMN," Anne remarked. She looked at Tom's annotation in the drawing and started remodeling the process.

On the canvas she introduced three new activities, each one dedicated to the teams that Tom mentioned. After that, she dragged a diamond shape with a plus to split the sequence flow and the same shape to join the branches that followed.

Tom took out his black notebook and browsed through the pages. He stopped at the XOR gateway and pointed at it, "That looks similar to the XOR gateway you showed me the other day."

"Oh, I remember, you noted that down in your notebook," Anne remarked. "Yes, that is right. In general, gateways are used to split or merge the sequence flow of a process." She pointed at the XOR gateway in Tom's notebook. "In this case, exactly one outgoing branch is taken when splitting and one branch is needed to proceed when joining. The other gateway here," Anne pointed at the screen, "is the parallel gateway. It means ..."

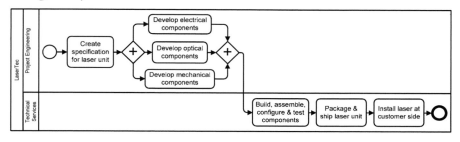

"Let me try," Tom interfered. "It probably means that all branches are taken."

"When splitting the sequence flow, correct," Anne completed his thoughts.

"Too easy ...," Tom leaned back in his chair.

"When joining, it waits for all incoming branches to complete," Anne finished the description.

"Yes, and that is exactly what happens here, the project engineers create an initial specification together and then they split up and work in parallel. When all the component development is done, they hand over the work to technical services." A bright smile came over Tom's face as he reviewed the process. Tom took some quick notes on a sheet of paper and jumped up from his seat.

"I think I can take it from here," he said and went to the door.

"Where are you heading?" Anne asked.

"I have some more ideas, but I have to play with them. Can you send me the model and the link to that process editor?"

"Sure," Anne replied, "I'll send you the link to the model. It's automatically stored online. I'll grant you access rights. If you load the URL, the editor will automatically come up in your browser."

Back in his office, Tom opened his notebook and made note of the new BPMN constructs that he had just learned from Anne. The new gateway and the role concept helped a lot in expressing the processes that were on his mind. But he was still unsatisfied. The documents that were produced and used during the process still weren't properly represented. Anne mentioned that information used in a process could be represented as well.

He would ask her about that tomorrow. But first, there was a weekend to fill. Work is done by people, and people need spare time to recover.

Parallel Gateway

When used to split the sequence flow, all outgoing branches are taken. When joining the flow, all branches must complete before the process continues.

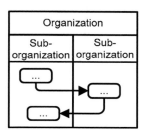

Pools and Lanes

Used to depict organizations or roles. A pool contains the process; lanes are optional and can sub-divide the pool or other lanes hierarchically. An activity is done by the role of the pool/lane which it is contained in.

Chapter 4

Information Flowing

When Tom entered his office after the weekend, his eyes landed on the notes he had taken the previous week. He started reading his email. He had received ten emails since last Friday. One by Haffner, one by Anne with the process model link, and eight pieces of spam. He started to read the email from Haffner.

```
Dear Mr. Bauer,

I'll be in the office on Tuesday morning. We
should meet for a status update on your work.
I heard that you have already talked to A.J.
about the engineering process.
Let's have a chat tomorrow morning at 9am.

Haffner
```

Tom was glad about Haffner's interest but still felt kind of unprepared. He had no proper process to show yet. He scanned Anne's email again to retrieve the link to the process model. Among his notes he found one sheet of paper with large letters on it saying "include sales." He remembered the quick chat with the senior sales manager. How could he have forgotten to take this into account on Friday?

Tom changed the process model, plugged in the changes, and continued to modify various parts. He dragged unknown modeling elements from the shape repository onto the canvas, inspected them, arranged them, re-arranged them, and then deleted them. In some cases the symbols didn't tell him anything. In other cases, he assumed that he had quite some understanding of their purpose. But toying around was not leading anywhere. He would work on this with Anne in the afternoon, if she was available.

"Hi, Tom," Anne welcomed him in her office.

"Are you busy?" Tom carefully asked.

"Not too much, just paperwork," Anne replied.

She seemed to be relaxed, with a constant smile on her face. Tom compared that with his own mood. In her case, family and children had provided good recreational activity over the weekend.

"I was waiting for you. I saw your email," Anne said.

"Yes, the email. I attached the refined model of the process from Friday. I worked on it today."

"Let's have a look."

Anne opened the tool and looked at the process.

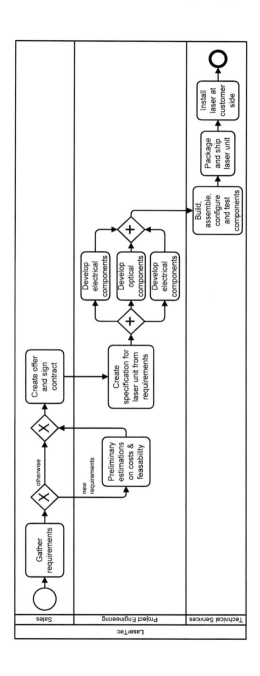

"Aha, you included sales in the picture," Anne said instantly.

"How do you like it?"

"It's a good idea. It gives the process a broader scope." Anne followed the process flow with her fingertips on the screen. "So, the sales guys contact project engineering to help them with the estimations. Really? Is that true?"

"Yes," Tom replied. He was a bit proud that Anne read and correctly explained his model.

"I knew it," Anne yelled. "These sales guys always pretend that they rock the house on their own. But they can't create a simple offer without help from us."

Ouch! Tom instantly felt that process transparency also had its trade-offs. With a process model at hand you don't only see what your own role in the organization is, but you also see the activities other people do.

"Good to know," she repeated her thought, "that the sales guys can't do everything on their own."

Tom felt the need to explain the model in more detail. "Well, this only happens in some cases. In other cases, sales can do this on their own."

"That's what you tried to say with 'otherwise' here?" Anne pointed at the sequence flow between the XOR gateways. "You might consider using the BPMN default flow for such a case," she said. Without waiting for Tom's reaction she changed the arrow to one with a backslash at the beginning, instead of the textual description.

"What does it mean?" Tom asked.

" 'Otherwise'. It means that if the other conditions, such as 'new requirements,' are not true then this is the flow to go," Anne said smirking.

"This is just a shortcut notation to say 'otherwise'?" he asked.

"Exactly. One of the branches has to be taken anyway. So, when none of the other criteria match, this default flow is used to indicate the sequence flow to take."

"Um, I'm not sure whether this is what I wanted to say." Tom took out his small black notebook and noted down the new element. "But is there something wrong with the process itself?"

"From a modeling perspective, no. And to my best knowledge I cannot see business-level mistakes in here either," Anne said. She saved the model and leaned back.

"What is this element?" Tom asked and pointed straight at an icon in the element box of the modeling program. It looked like a sheet of paper with a dog-ear. Tom had some hopes that it would help him to proceed with the model.

"This is a data object," Anne explained. "It is used to represent information like documents used in your process."

"Such as a contract," Tom thought aloud.

"Sure, any kind of information."

Anne didn't seem interested in this modeling element but Tom felt that it's a new dimension. He cut out the first part of his process and pasted it to a new canvas. After some rearrangement, he dragged a data object from the element box and named it "contract." He took a sequence flow and connected the "Create offer and sign contract" activity with the "contract" data object.

Anne observed him without interrupting. So, he continued creating a "specification" data object and connected it to the "create specification from requirements" activity in the same way. Then he stopped and looked at Anne waiting for a reaction. "What does it mean?" she finally asked.

Tom tried to explain his intention. "It is supposed to mean that these documents are produced by the activities they are connected with."

"Well, your intuitive understanding of BPMN's data flow abilities is quite good. Maybe it's worth spending some time here." She took over the mouse and started by deleting the sequence flow that Tom had just drawn between the activities and the data objects. "This was wrong," she said. "You want to express information flowing, right? This is different from control logic in the process."

"I see." Tom was concentrating.

"BPMN has a specific connector to represent that." She dragged an arrow with a dotted line and then redrew the activity-data connections Tom had drawn.

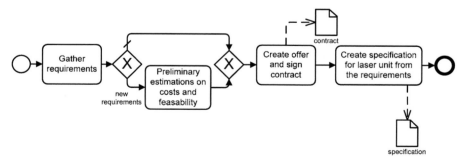

"Well," Tom was barely impressed, "then I was almost right. It's just looking slightly different."

"It is fundamentally different. BPMN is a control-flow-driven language. The order of execution in a process is determined using the sequence flow. Data objects can be used to express things on top."

"So, that's why it has a dotted line similar to the textual annotation. It has the same meaning, namely nothing," Tom said with an unsuppressed disappointment in his voice.

"Well, there is more in there," Anne explained. "See, the arrows indicate the direction in which the information flows." Anne pointed at the "specification" data object. "Here, the information is produced. There can be situations where the information is consumed. Let's think about it."

"If they do a preliminary study, then the information would be used to create an offer," he said.

"Yes, of course," Anne replied, "here we produce a preliminary study and then we use it over there." She created a new data object and named it "preliminary study." Then she created a directed association pointing at it from the activity "preliminary estimations." Another directed association connects the data object with the "create offer" activity.

"You see that there is value in here?" Anne asked.

She looked at Tom. Tom was staring at the computer screen without saying a word. He saw value, but he was not yet ready to jump on and run with it. Anne recognized this.

"I need a break," she said and left the room.

While Anne was gone, Tom took her place at the computer. He looked at the model, played with possible re-arrangements and added new data objects to the canvas, "customer requirements" and "contracted requirements." He continued to connect the information to activities.

When Anne came back into the room she walked straight to the coffee machine. She observed Tom while filling up her cup. He was absolutely focused.

"How's it going?" she asked as if they had not seen each other earlier that day.

"I think it makes sense. I can make use of the data object to show which information is produced, respectively needed, in a particular part of the process. Is there more to it?" Tom asked and looked up at Anne.

"Not much. If a document is modified during a process step, you can denote this by using a bidirected association."

"You mean, an association with an arrow at each side." Tom looked at his process model. "Not in here." Tom took out his small black notebook and started noting something down.

Anne took her coffee and went over to Tom. She scanned the process snippet that Tom had heavily enriched with data objects and data flow.

"The contract requirements," Anne pointed at the screen, "They are only produced here and used exactly in the activity afterwards."

"Yes," Tom looked up at the screen, "the information is actually exclusive to these two activities. Is there a more elegant way to express that?"

"Indeed there is. You can associate the document directly with the sequence flow." Anne changed the process model.

"Nice," Tom said and continued writing down details in his book. "Can I do the same with the preliminary studies?"

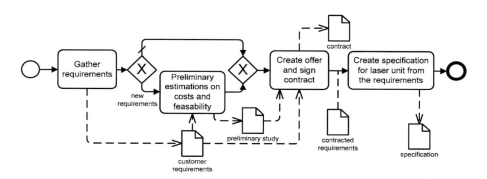

"Well, the association to the sequence flow is a shortcut notation for a particular case. Since there is the XOR gateway between the activities using the preliminary study data object, you can not apply it."

Tom grabbed the mouse and saved the model. Then he went back to the original model and started to put in the data objects and connections. Anne pointedly looked at the clock over her office door.

"May I ask you to do this stuff on your own computer? There is actually some work I have to finish."

"Oh. Sure."

Tom saved the models so that he could access them from his computer. He stood up, took his notebook, and went to the door. There he stopped and turned around to Anne.

"Thanks for your time, Anne," he said.

"You're welcome," Anne replied and smiled at him.

When Tom returned to his office, he proceeded from where he stopped before. He took his overall process idea, put in all the documents he could imagine, and associated them with the activities in his process. Afterwards, he printed it on paper and put it on the wall of his office. He was satisfied with his work. This would be the main artifact to communicate the progress to Haffner, he thought.

It was 8:55 a.m. when Tom entered his office the next morning. He was surprised to find Haffner already there. He stood in the office and inspected the printed process model on the wall. From the side, Tom could see Haffner's silhouette. He noticed that Haffner's belly made his way well beyond his belt. "Good morning, Mr. Bauer," Haffner welcomed Tom. "Unfortunately, I am short of time this morning, that's why I came here. Can you quickly update me on your status?"

"Yes, Sir. I was talking to people from sales and project engineering. Then I tried to bring the overall process into a big picture," Tom explained.

"You mean this picture here?" Haffner pointed at the printout on the wall. "What is this?"

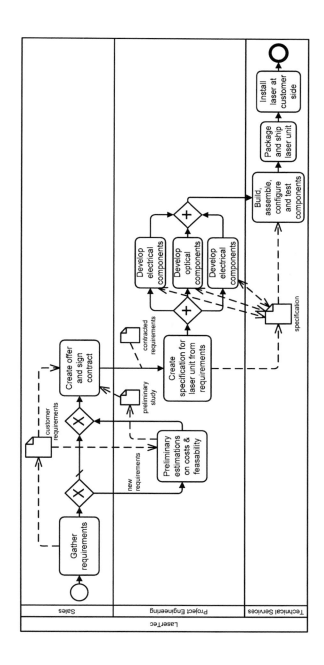

"It is a process model written in BPMN, the Business Process Modeling Notation. It is a modeling language to depict and communicate processes." Tom pointed at the pool element to start explaining the notation, "This is a pool. It can contain processes ..."

"I don't want to become a modeling expert, Mr. Bauer. Just tell me what we are doing," Haffner said impatiently.

He explained the process, starting with the work the sales guys do. While explaining, he made his way through the model by pointing at the process parts that he was talking about. Haffner listened and nodded his head from time to time to keep Tom going. With his fingers he could point at the part that he was currently talking about, and he could avoid confusion about the context. The longer he talked the more confident he became.

Haffner suddenly interrupted him, "I don't think you have fully understood what we do, Mr. Bauer."

Tom stared at Haffner, anticipating further shocks to come. Haffner smiled at him and started explaining.

"We do not always build all the components for a laser." He paused and emptied his coffee before continuing. "This company is more than thirty years old. We can't afford reinventing the wheel for each project. I'm pretty sure that we have component specifications at hand that we reuse. Without asking them, the project engineers will probably not tell you, but I am confident that a significant amount of component specifications are already there. And what is the meaning of all these arrows?" Haffner pointed at the specification data object.

"The specification is created once and is then the basis for further work. However, as development goes on, the specification is modified, and refined as further details become clearer. Finally, it is the input for the build and assembly step."

"But what is the meaning of all these different types of arrows?" Haffner asked.

"They show where documents are created, modified or read in the process," Tom explained.

"Imagine you are run over by a truck tomorrow," Haffner said, "all that remains is this." He pointed at the model. "It documents your knowledge. Do you think it's adequately represented?"

"I will fix this component development stuff and write a document to explain...."

Haffner interrupted, "Don't get me wrong, Mr. Bauer. I think modeling processes is a great thing to document knowledge. I have seen this stuff before from Ms. White. But you have to be more accurate. Otherwise a reader will have difficulties gaining all the implicit knowledge. It might also happen that I might have to learn from your process models. But I feel lost with so many elements and so many arrows going into all directions. You need to focus on the message."

Tom looked at the diagram and then looked back to Haffner. He walked over to the window of his small office and looked down at the street.

"What information are you missing?," Tom asked.

"You told me about our sales activities, all this reviewing of old projects and stuff. I think this should be documented in the same way," Haffner said.

Tom nodded his head. He turned around and leaned against the window. Haffner walked a loop around the small office, went back to the model on the wall, and pointed at the end of the process.

"And what are these service guys doing? When I was involved in the development myself we were also testing and installing the units at the customer site. I never understood why we needed these guys at all. And you know what? Ever since we have had them, this part of the production process," he encircled the last three activities with his finger, "takes longer and longer."

Haffner was totally into it. "I need to know more about this. What are they doing and why is it taking so long?" Haffner walked over to Tom who was still leaning at the window. "I want you to have a deeper look. Capturing the processes is nice, but without a really deep knowledge about the reasons behind the process you won't be able to fully understand."

Tom looked down and nodded his head.

Haffner encouraged Tom, "I think you're well on your way. But you'll have to take it further. I need you to also look behind the processes and give me a management summary." He threw away his empty coffee cup.

Tom stood in front of his model for another ten minutes. There would be much more information to be presented in a single model, he thought. How could that fit together with a management summary? He would need some more time with Anne that was for sure. But he also decided to spend some time with the men in the blue suits, the technical services guys.

Default Flow
The default sequence flow taken at an XOR gateway. If no other condition matches then the default flow is taken as a fall back.

Data object

Data Object
Represents information flowing through the process such as documents, emails, faxes, or letters.

Directed Association
Used to associate data objects with activities. The arrow indicates the information flow, such as reading or writing the data object.

Bidirected Association
Also used to associate data objects with activities. The arrows at both sides indicate that the data object is read and written, so modified during the execution of the activity.

Undirected Association
Can be used to associate data objects with the sequence flow in between two activities. Represents data a shortcut for data written and directly read afterwards.

Chapter 5

The Need for More

Meeting the right people turned out to be harder than expected. The sales guys were all out on business assignments. Tom had to recall the sales details from the chat with the senior sales manager, Ben Baker, the other day. The next stakeholders were the project engineers. But since Winning was on vacation, Tom had to find another person willing to talk to him. Tom decided to invite one of the project engineers for lunch. During lunch, Tom tried to get back to the develop-or-reuse problem toward which Haffner pointed him. Martin, the thirty-year-old engineer, told him that it was always a mix of different things. Most components were developed by reusing earlier work and modifying it. In some cases they could completely re-use pre-developed component specifications, which they could copy and paste into the current specification document.

To gather more information, Tom walked to the factory building to see the guys from technical services. He was surprised to find them busy disassembling the machine that popped out cylinders into a basket the other day. He stood aside and watched them working for some minutes. Then he introduced himself to the man supervising the work. He learned that this guy is in charge of re-assembling the machine next week in Portugal. That is why he had to oversee the whole disassembling and packaging.

"How long have you been working on this laser unit?" Tom asked.

"This baby took us seven weeks now," the man replied. "It has gotten more complicated because this one has to integrate into the assembly line at the customer site."

Tom nodded and stood aside. He did not want to get in the way. These men were concentrating and busy.

"So there were seven weeks of assembly and testing?" Tom asked in order to continue the conversation.

The man turned to Tom and motioned for him to follow him. They walked down the factory floor and started a long conversation about the role of technical services. It went on for half an hour, while Tom only nodded his head and listened.

Totally filled with information, he thanked his new friend and went back to his office. For the rest of the day he could only think about the detailed descriptions of the process and how they fit into the big picture.

Later, Tom met Anne in her office.

"You know," Tom started, "I was showing the process to Haffner the other day and...."

Interested, Anne interrupted, "How did he like it?"

"Well, he generally saw the value of process modeling," Tom started, "but he was not satisfied with the actual content of the models. He wants more accurate information and neat models at the same time. I'm not sure I can do this with BPMN."

"You want some more lessons on BPMN?" Anne asked.

"Probably I need more," Tom replied. "I have talked to a number of people already. I will also interview some others, but I need more understanding of the notation to adequately capture what I learn."

"Is that what Haffner told you?" Anne asked compassionately.

"It's what I feel when I start modeling," Tom replied.

Anne pointed at the chair Tom usually sat in when he was in her office. Tom took the chair over to sit next to Anne.

"Do you already know what you are looking for?" Anne asked.

"Yes," Tom said, and he took out some folded sheets of paper from his pocket. He unfolded them and pointed at some crossed out sketches on the first sheet.

"You told me about the gateways," Tom started. "There is one where you take and join all branches...."

"The AND gateway," Anne interposed.

"There is one that selects and joins exactly one branch."

"That would be the XOR gateway," Anne thought aloud.

Tom took a deep breath before continuing, "And now I have a situation that does not fit either one or the other extreme. I need something to express that an arbitrary number of branches can be taken."

"An inclusive OR," Anne mumbled.

Tom was astonished. He did not expect it to be so easy to convince Anne about the need for another gateway type. During the last few days he had tried to assemble the intended semantics with combinations of AND and XOR gateways but did not succeed. He was expecting Anne to correctly remodel the process with him. Instead, Anne grabbed a pen and started sketching three process snippets on the paper just below his own crossed out sketches.

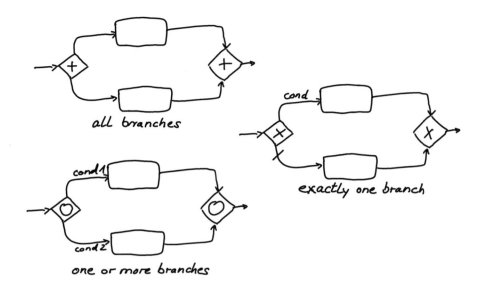

all branches

cond

exactly one branch

cond1

cond2

one or more branches

"You're right, Tom," said Anne, while completing her sketch. "In some situations you need to express that different paths are taken based on independent conditions." She pointed at the structure in the middle, depicting XOR gateways. "Here you can only take one branch. Not more, not less. The default branch denotes the way to go in case none of the conditions is true."

"Yes," Tom answered. "We talked about this the other day. But how can I ensure that only one condition is true?"

"It's up to the modeler to ensure that. That's her responsibility."

"Um... okay," Tom grumbled.

"But with the Inclusive OR gateway," Anne proceeded, "you can give each outgoing sequence flow an individual condition."

"So, if all conditions are true, it behaves like an AND gateway and if only one condition is true it's an XOR gateway," Tom thought aloud.

"That's right. But you would only use this construct in a situation where you can not say for sure how many branches will be taken."

"I see. But what if none of the conditions is true?"

"Again you, as a modeler, have to address that because if no condition is true, the process will get stuck," Anne said.

"Um ... so if I want to merge those branches again. I can use the same gateway, right? And it will wait for those branches which have been activated by the splitting Inclusive OR gateway?"

"Yes. You can also use the Inclusive OR gateway to merge branches. But this part is tricky because theoretically you can combine all gateways and use an AND split together with an Inclusive OR merge gateway. But then the semantics become much more complicated. This makes it hard to understand and communicate the process model. So, my advice is that you use pairs of splits and joints of the same gateway whenever possible. For the Inclusive OR gateway, that means you wait for exactly those tokens that have been created by the corresponding Inclusive OR split gateway beforehand."

Tom looked at the sketch. The Inclusive OR gateway seemed to fit perfectly into his needs. He put the sheet of paper under the pile of unfolded papers he brought with him. The next top most paper had a big headline stating "Sales."

"I can also use the Inclusive OR gateway to express the sales work. They do different things in a very unstructured way. When they gather the requirements they have some work packages and are free to choose what they do in order to accomplish the task."

"Well, this sounds different. The Inclusive OR gateway should only be used if the work packages to be done are preselected by conditions. That does not fit your description."

Anne scanned through the notes that Tom had taken. She struggled to read his handwriting. So he explained the process part and gave her some insight into the way the sales men work.

"The work you describe here is unconstrained and free, with wide options about what to do," Anne said. "To gather the requirements, the salesperson could do different things in any order. To start or skip an activity is his choice. Also he could decide to interview the customer as many times as he likes. That does not fit into a structured process flow."

Tom was disappointed, "Does that mean there is no proper way to model this in BPMN?"

"Oh. yes, there is. You are not the first one having this problem. In BPMN they introduced a construct called Ad Hoc subprocess."

"Okay, and what exactly does it do?" Tom asked expectantly.

"Exactly that!" Anne turned to her computer and started dragging shapes onto the canvas. From Tom's notes she identified the work to be done. Tom helped her pick the correct tasks and interpret his handwriting.

"I remembered the model the other day. It had this activity – gather requirements," Anne started explaining. "What we do here is, we drill down into that activity and specify what has to be done to accomplish it."

"I didn't know you can just drill down into activities," Tom exclaimed. "Can I do this with other activities as well?"

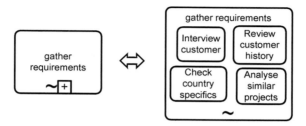

"Sure, but, before that, let's talk about the semantics of the Ad Hoc subprocess." Anne pointed at the shape while explaining, "So inside an Ad Hoc subprocess you can place tasks only! " Anne paused and looked into Tom's eyes to emphasize the importance of this message. "All tasks may be executed in any order. The performer, the one actually doing this, decides for the next task. He's also free to do these tasks as often as he likes."

"Even including no execution?" Tom interrupted.

"Yes, even no execution at all," Anne smiled.

Tom stared at the computer screen, "Yeah, that perfectly fits his job. The salesperson is free to do or skip whatever task."

"Good, so that's it," Anne said.

"Okay, let's come back to this drill-down thing," Tom pushed.

Anne wanted to take a sip of coffee. The cup was empty already. With a teasing smile she asked, "Why are you so interested in subprocesses?"

"You know, Haffner wants me to present a management summary. On the other hand, he wants an accurate and detailed model of the reality. I assume that the new model will not fit on one page. So, I have to find a way to hide information and drill into it on demand."

"Yes, hierarchical models are ideal for that, and subprocesses in BPMN support exactly this concept. If you want to express that there is more behind one activity, you can just place a plus into it. That means it is a subprocess."

"So there is a process behind the activity and I can drill down into it," Tom repeated.

Anne explained, "Subprocesses can be used to place a whole process model inside. Usually a subprocess links to a process diagram described somewhere else. But there is also the concept of embedded subprocesses. They can be expanded to show the process behind the subprocess in the same diagram."

"That makes sense – so I can show or hide information within a process model," Tom remarked.

"Yes. Let's have a look at an example." Anne opened an empty canvas in her modeling tool. "Do you have any idea which process part you want to discuss for this?"

"Oh yes!" Tom went through the pile of pages in front of him. He finally found the one he wanted. "Here," he said, "I think the technical services process suits quite well."

"Aha," Anne said without looking at Tom's paper. She took a sip of coffee and pushed the mouse toward Tom. Without hesitating, Tom took the mouse and started modeling. He chose subprocesses instead of tasks for those activities he wanted to decompose.

When Tom had finished modeling, he gave the mouse back to Anne. Without saying a word, Anne took it and double-clicked the first subprocess symbol in the process. One dialog later she could drag and drop modeling elements into the subprocess shape. The subprocess marker disappeared. Almost bored, Anne put three activities in a sequence and connected them.

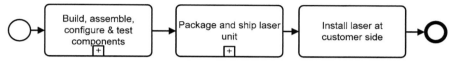

"Shouldn't there be a start and an end event?" Tom asked.

"Where?"

"In the subprocess? he asked.

"Well, no. I mean yes. You're right, but you can use a shortcut notation like this. It means that the subprocess starts with the activity that has no incoming sequence flow, and it ends when all activities are done."

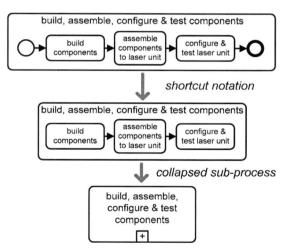

Anne copied and pasted the subprocess and remodeled it with a start and an end event. "For our cases these are totally equivalent representations of the same information," Anne explained.

Tom frowned, "Why would I do this? Two representations with the same meaning?"

"Well, you can have a more compact representation of the same information. Embedded subprocesses are shown in the same diagram. So there is limited space."

"I see."

"And usually you want to avoid overhead to have the most compact representation possible."

"Um.., I understand the motivation," Tom said, "but still I think it's odd that one can do it both ways."

"If you think that is odd, have a look at this."

Anne created a new process model and started modeling. She took a subprocess without a marker and placed two other activities inside without a connection.

"Can you imagine what that means?" She asked.

"It looks a bit like the Ad Hoc subprocess. But we are missing the marker here," Tom replied.

"That's right. This is also a shortcut notation." Anne put another process snippet next to it.

"This representation says," Anne explained, "that both activities inside the subprocess are enabled as soon as the subprocess is enabled. When these activities are done, the subprocess finishes. It's a shortcut notation to say: These activities can run in parallel."

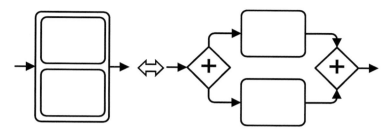

"Um, strange," Tom stated. "Why not simply take the other version using gateways to express parallelism?"

"Just look at the size," Anne defended the approach. "We can express the same knowledge with much less space."

"But only for this particular case. If there were more activities with complex relations, what then?"

"I agree," Anne interrupted, "but for this case it helps to save space and constructs. That's why I said it's a shortcut."

Anne saved the models they created so far. When she came to the technical services process, Tom interfered. "Can we also refine this process a little more? I don't think it is properly represented yet."

"Sure."

Tom pointed at the task "build components" and said, "here, there is something interesting going on that I was not able to express. It is also related to parallelism."

"Okay, let's have a look," Anne said.

"You know, they build these components and therefore they split up. The creation of a single component is decoupled from the creation of any other." Tom paused for a moment before he continued,

"But I don't know how to express this. In general, I don't know how many components will be produced."

"Um....I'm not sure. A normal activity representing the whole step would be the correct way to show it," Anne suggested.

"But there must be more to it," Tom replied. "I want to express that there are numerous components built. They usually do it in parallel, so theoretically, if there were five components and five people working on them, they could do it all in parallel."

"Ah, I think I got the point." Anne picked up the ball, "The activity to build a component is done many, many times."

"Yes, for each component."

"And each execution is independent, so they might overlap."

"Yes, for me it's just a special case for parallelism but it's always the same task," Tom said.

"That has the characteristics of a multiple instances activity," Anne finally concluded.

"Okay," Tom was confused, "that doesn't ring a bell."

Anne placed a marker with three bars below the activity.

"That should do," she said.

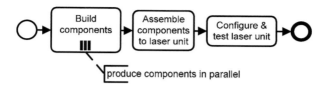

Tom stared at the screen, disbelieving. "And what does it mean now?"

"It means that the activity is executed many times, once for each component," Anne explained. "The individual executions are independent from each other, so they can run in parallel."

"How do you call that activity type again?"

"A multiple instances activity."

"Okay, the name makes sense, but the marker is strange." Tom grabbed the mouse and put an annotation to the activity.

"It's just for me to remember," he said.

Thinking about it, he asked, "When is this activity completed? Can I skip instances just like I can for the Ad Hoc subprocess?"

Anne rejected emphatically, "No, no, no! Ad Hoc subprocesses offer inner activities and the user decides to do one or the other. The multiple instances activity can express that each item in a list should be processed."

"Ah, like each component in our case."

"Yes. Or writing an email to each person on a list."

"I see," Tom nodded. He stared out of the window and into the blue sky. Anne observed him. She could see his brain working.

"So whenever I do the same task many times, I can use this."

"Not quite correct," Anne replied. "First of all, it is not limited to tasks. You can also have a subprocess that is done multiple times, okay?"

Tom nodded his head. He had taken out his black notebook and started noting things down.

"Also, there are other ways to express that an activity is done multiple times. The distinguishing feature of the multiple instances activity is that these things run in parallel and typically the number of instances depends on a collection of items to be processed."

"I got this part, but what do you mean by 'other ways'?"

"Loops, for example." Anne paused to await Tom's reaction. He didn't raise an eyebrow waiting for more information to come.

Anne turned toward the computer screen. "Here," she pointed at the model. "The testing is probably not done once, is it?"

"Oh no, I talked to the guys from technical services and they always test, configure, test, configure ... This goes on for weeks! "

"See, that's what I mean," Anne said. She took an arrow indicating a circle and placed it as a marker at the bottom of the activity "configure & test laser unit."

"And what does that mean? Is the task repeated?" Tom asked.

"Yes."

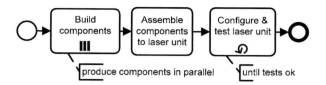

"How often is it repeated?"

"Well, you have to specify that of course. It's done using a condition. You know, not everything you can express with BPMN is represented visually. There are quite a number of hidden attributes for each construct." Anne pointed to the attribute list on the right of the tool. "The tool allows us to configure the hidden attributes. But at the end of the day, it's all about the visual diagram. When you print it, you won't see all the attribute values. Therefore, I would suggest an additional annotation to also visually show the attribute." She associated an annotation to the activity and put in "until tests ok."

"Um...." Tom took a long pause to think about it.

"Sorry, I have to leave," Anne said to Tom and started packing some paper into a briefcase.

"Couldn't I just model loops using XOR gateways?" Tom asked.

"You can, of course. The loop activity is again just a shortcut."

She rushed to the door, turned around and looked at Tom. He still stared at the computer screen, lost in thoughts.

"You can stay here if you like. I'll be back soon." She paused for a moment and then said, "Maybe it's a good exercise to model the looped activity as a subprocess. But beware," she lifted a finger, "the loop marker is already stating a loop. You should take a normal subprocess and model the loop inside using gateways." Then she left.

Tom was still sitting in front of the computer screen. He started browsing through the models. From time to time he took some notes. After that he started remodeling the configure and test laser unit activity. "Beware!" Tom could still hear Anne's advice. After he finished the model, he started looking around Anne's office. She had huge plants in there. Tom wondered whether she had raised them here or brought them from home. Through the window, he could already see Anne coming back from the factory building. He checked his model again, decided to make some changes, and played with the arrangement of elements in the embedded subprocess. Then he printed it out and waited for Anne.

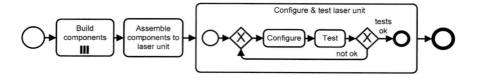

"And? How did it go?" Anne asked while walking through the door of her office.

"Quite good, I think," Tom replied and proudly held up the printed model.

"Uh ...," Anne said while taking the model from Tom's hands.

"Let's see. This model says that you will in any case first configure and then test." She took the model over to the coffee machine. When she recognized that the coffee pot was empty, she put the model aside, and filled the coffee machine.

"So when the tests are okay, you finish. When the tests are not okay, you loop back. How is that possible?" Anne wondered.

"What?" Tom wanted to know.

"Why did you join the branches in the beginning using an XOR gateway?"

"Well, I thought it can be used to join alternative branches. And in this case there is either the start coming in or the loop back. I thought of these as alternatives."

"That's correct," Anne assured Tom. "That's totally correct. I'm just astonished that you got it right the very first time you try that."

"Originally, I connected it back to the start event because the process starts all over. Would that also be valid?"

"Definitely not. A start event must never have an incoming sequence flow. Just as the end event must not have an outgoing one," Anne explains.

"So there is nothing wrong about this model?" Tom wondered. He really expected mistakes in there. This was the first loop he ever modeled.

Anne briefly inspected the model, "No, I don't see any. I have only one remark since you are now approaching a more sophisticated modeling style, and we even talked about shortcuts ...," Anne paused.

"That is?" Tom couldn't wait for the answer.

"If you loop back directly into the configuration activity, you would save the XOR gateway," Anne replied. "The semantics are, that an activity is triggered by an incoming sequence flow. So, you could do an implicit merge by connecting two alternative sequence flows into one activity."

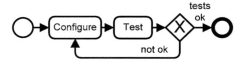

"Um.,…" Tom stared at the diagram. "In this case I can save some space and could have a more condensed model. But actually I don't like all this shortcut stuff."

"That's okay, just normal. You have to practice and then you will find one or the other solution more useful. I just wanted to make you aware of alternatives," Anne said. At the same time, she glanced at the clock above the door.

"I want more!" Tom exclaimed. He was in a rush now. Ready to model everything. "Please teach me more concepts."

"No way," Anne replied. "I have to leave now and pick up my son from my mother's place. Besides, you're well equipped already. Go, model! And come back if you have questions."

Inclusive OR Gateway
Can be used to split or join the sequence flow. When splitting, branches are taken based on individual conditions, but at least one branch should be taken. When joining, all activated branches are synchronized.

Collapsed Subprocess
Is a special activity that contains a process model inside. One can expand it to see the embedded process within the same diagram. Alternatively, a subprocess can link to a process model somewhere else.

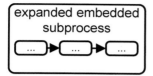

Expanded Embedded Subprocess

When expanding the subprocess, one can see the detailed behavior. Shortcuts are allowed such as omitting start and end events, making them implicit.

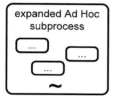

Expanded Ad Hoc Subprocess

Contains tasks only. The performer of the tasks can decide to do, re-do or skip them. The order can be freely chosen.

Multiple Instances Activity

The activity is done many times for each item in a collection. The instances can be spawned off in parallel if enough resources are available.

Loop Activity

The activity is done repeatedly. The number of executions depends on a condition to be checked either at start or at completion of one activity instance.

Chapter 6

Complex Situations Require Simple Models

Within days Tom had created more than twenty models. They all depicted pieces and parts of the development process. Some fit together neatly – others had overlaps or white spots. He also captured the same situation with alternative models to discuss them with the people involved. He often needed to explain the meaning of the different symbols before the interviewees were willing to comment on the models. However, the only person to give detailed feedback about his models remained Anne. They often discussed modeling mistakes and the modeling style. From the notes taken during the interviews Tom identified the information to be depicted. But he struggled to put everything together in one big picture.

A couple of days later, Tom was finally there. From the set of process models he managed to create one overall model. It showed an end-to-end process starting with sales and ending with the laser unit running at the customer site. He was very satisfied to finally have an integrated view of the overall process. When he printed it out, the model spanned six pages.

"You will not show that to Haffner, will you?" Anne marveled when Tom showed her the process modeling puzzle covering his office wall.

"Oh, no," Tom replied. "That is definitely not the model to discuss with Haffner. But I'm not sure how to tackle this. I thought about omitting this part...."

"Hierarchical modeling," Anne interrupted. "You may leave things out. But you'll gain the most from a set of interlinked hierarchical models."

Tom was lost. "Are we talking about subprocesses?"

"Exactly. You will have to slice the process into reasonable parts. Each part is representing a subprocess. These subprocesses should fit together into one top-level process for the big picture."

"But it's difficult to slice it. There are many alternatives to break the process into pieces. How to choose?"

"Yeah, that's difficult. This is a decision you as the modeler of this process will have to take," Anne said. Tom was disappointed. Anne's answer was not of any help. He had expected a more solid grounding for his work.

"As a rule of thumb," Anne advised, "one model should fit on one page. Readable! "

After Anne left his office, Tom tried to identify process parts to summarize as subprocesses. But where to start and to end? How to bundle activities together, so they form a reasonable subprocess?

These questions drove Tom day in, day out. They even came back to him at night in a dream! He was driving a golf cart. Winning, Haffner, and Anne were accompanying him. The driveway was actually a sequence flow. When they came to a crossroad, it turned out to be an XOR gateway. Tom set the indicator to continue at the default flow.

"That's not how we do it," Winning said. Haffner gently reached for the steering wheel and redirected the cart. They continued driving down the other path. They passed tasks like "create specification" and "assemble unit." The tasks were painted on the ground like a crosswalk. Tom drove on. The drive way narrowed, and the golf cart sped up. A block appeared on the horizon.

"What shall I do?" Tom asked nervously. The block was getting bigger as the golf cart gets nearer. It looked like a high riser with a huge plus on it.

"Stop here, it's not important," Anne said from the back seat.

"Go on," Haffner commanded, "I want to know everything! "

The block was getting bigger as the golf cart gathered speed. Tom tried to slow down but the brakes didn't react. Tom yelled as they were about to crash into the wall of the big block. He awoke from his dream dripping with sweat. It was five o'clock in the morning. The early birds had just started screaming in front of his bedroom. What a dream. What a night.

Back in the office, Tom cleaned up the models, which were spread all over the walls and the floor. One snippet he found was the initial development process that he drew with Anne at the very beginning. Only five activities. Tom decided to focus on this top-level process and adjust all the rest to it. With this decision taken he could now model the process top-down. The work really seemed to flow, and Tom could finally reduce the zoo of process models to a core set that described the big picture. He was not confident about his decision because it also meant throwing away models he was very proud of. But Anne assured him that this is how it works in the real world.

"You will never model the complete reality," she said. "You need to focus on the main purpose of your models. The more complex the situation, the more important it is to focus. Complex situations require simple models."

With that certainty, Tom finally called Haffner and made an appointment to present the development process at LaserTec to him. Haffner limited the presentation to fifteen minutes. The whole meeting was to last only half an hour. Tom had expected more time, but Haffner made it clear that the value was to communicate the important stuff in condensed form. For a convenient presentation, Tom assembled a slide set. Each slide contained one of his small process models. When Tom came to the meeting room, Haffner sat at the head of the table browsing through paperwork. "Shall we start?" Haffner asked and briefly looked up to Tom. When he saw that the projector was not running yet, he lowered his head again, "Are you set, Mr. Bauer?"

Tom powered up the projector and started the presentation from his flash-memory stick. Once the first slide was shown on the wall, Haffner put his paper work aside and looked at Tom.

"Alright," Tom started, "Today I want to present an overview of the development process at LaserTec."

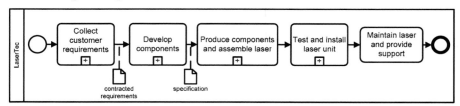

The first slide showed the top-level process. Tom explained the overall picture – first, the main activities, from collecting requirements to support at the customer side. Haffner was fully concentrated and followed Tom's description of the process. His eyes started shining when Tom explained the subprocess concept and that he was going to drill down into every process step marked with a plus. After a short introduction, Tom zoomed into the 'Collect customer requirements' subprocess. "You remember the sales activities," he started. "You requested to have the detailed activities in the process model and here they are." Tom explained the different steps that the sales colleagues conduct to gather the customer requirements.

"What is this tilde symbol good for?" Haffner interrupted.

"It denotes the fact, that each activity might be skipped or done while they gather requirements."

"Who decides to skip an activity?" Haffner wanted to know.

"The individual sales person. It's basically a set of activities that are offered to be done."

"Okay, so when is this step over?"

"When the customer requirements document is completed."

"Do we have a template for that document?"

"I'm not completely sure…." Tom had no straight answer: a question he never thought of, especially since this document, which he had shown Haffner a few weeks ago, was already in the process.

"Never mind. I will ask Anne to check this." Haffner noted something down on a blank sheet of paper.

"Then," Tom started again, "the salesperson might ask a project engineer to do some preliminary estimations."

"In case the requirements are new, I see," Haffner said as he completed the description.

"Yes, and, finally, sales creates a contract offer which is then signed by the customer. The contract is based on the customer requirements and, if necessary, on the preliminary study."

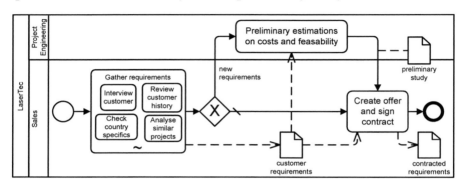

"Um...," Haffner mumbled. He reflected on the process, but looked a little unhappy. "In general, I like the level of detail here," Haffner said, "but getting a customer to sign a contract offer is a long process. Sometimes it never happens. All that is not reflected here. It looks as if the customer will do it anyway, no matter what we offer him." Haffner paused briefly before he continued, "Have you talked to sales about this?"

"This particular part?" Tom pointed at the 'Create offer and sign contract' activity. "Well, not in detail."

"Would it be possible to put such a plus into the shape and drill down to explore this activity?" Haffner asked.

"Yes, of course," Tom answered. He actually wanted to do that but he did not have enough information to model the situation. Therefore, he had dropped it.

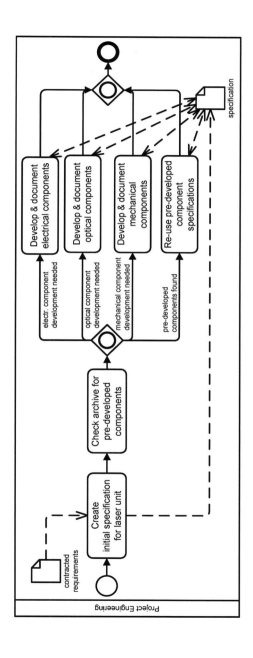

"The result of this first subprocess is," Tom started again while pointing at the overview diagram, "a set of requirements promised to the customer." He jumped back to the high-level process. "As you see here, this is passed to the next step in which the laser is developed."

"So the component development is done by project engineering," Tom said and pointed at the pool. "Starting from the contracted requirements, the initial specification for the laser unit is created. This is typically done in a workshop where all the engineers sit together. Then they split up and develop the necessary components."

Haffner was confused. "Didn't you miss something?" he interrupted and pointed at the projected image on the wall.

Tom stopped and turned around. He followed the process flow from the beginning and said, "Oh, yes ... of course." He rolled back the story line to the specification part, "When the specification is done, they look up in the archive whether they have already developed components like this; if so, they can reuse them."

"Wouldn't they just use the specifications for that?" Haffner wondered.

"I beg your pardon?"

"When they look up whether a particular component was already built before, I think the specification would be helpful. In your model the specification is connected to every activity but this one."

"Ahem...." Tom did not expect Haffner to pinpoint such details of the model.

"What are these diamonds with circles inside?" Haffner asked.

Tom was still confused about the last remark, but happy to

change the topic and explain the semantics of the inclusive OR gateway. He stressed the fact that each outgoing branch might be chosen and that the set of branches depended on individual expressions. That way, one or more – even all – branches might be chosen. Haffner was satisfied. He recalled the discussions on this topic that they had in Tom's office the other day.

"So, here you say that it might be possible that we do not develop mechanical components' specifications because we can reuse parts."

"That's right," Tom said.

"Okay, so what comes next? Where does the specification go?"

Tom jumped back to the top-level process and briefly resumed the process so far. "After the component developments are done, we have a detailed specification at hand. This is now used to produce the individual parts and to assemble them to a laser unit."

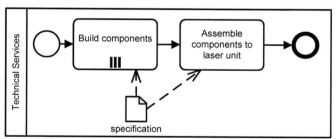

Haffner looked at the rather small process and frowned. "What is the point here? There are only two activities." Then he discovered the three bars in the "Build components" activity. "What are these?"

"Well," Tom started explaining, "they indicate that the activities are done multiple times. So, depending on the number of components to be built, there might be five or fifty activities of this type."

"Okay, that makes sense."

"The special fact here is," Tom continued, "that these activities are independent from each other. So if fifty components are to be built and we had the capacity, they can all be done in parallel. If we only have five workers, we can expect that it will take ten times as long."

"Well, the problem is not only the workforce," Haffner stated. "We need specialized machines to build the components. Last year we evaluated whether it makes sense to buy more machines to speed up exactly this part of the production that you are pointing at now. But the conclusion was that more machines wouldn't pay off. They are expensive, and more machines wouldn't significantly help to speed up the time from order to delivery." Haffner paused for a moment before he continued, "Then we thought the problem was the assembly of the laser units because more components need more time. But this was not a big deal either."

Haffner stared at the process model on the slide. He was lost in thought. Tom patiently waited for a reaction.

"Can you go back to your overview process?" Haffner asked, and Tom switched to the initial slides.

"There!" Haffner raised his arm and pointed at the process model. "That's where we lose most of the time. I still don't understand why. Can we dive into this?"

"I guess you mean the next process step, the one for testing and installation."

"Yes, of course. Just show me what happens there."

Tom zoomed into the subprocess for testing and installation, and the slide changed to the subprocess.

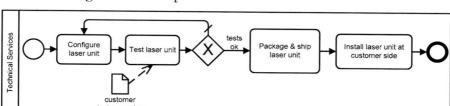

Tom took a step toward the slide projected on the wall and started describing, "There are a few reasons why the testing may take a long period of time. Most importantly, the cumulative complexity you mentioned before. But there is also the aspect of more integration with the machines at the customer site."

Tom illustrated the current project in which the laser unit had to integrate with the assembly line at the customer site and therefore needed specialized test scenarios. From his interviews he found out that in the majority of cases the customer provided test scenarios, but the detailed descriptions arrive just before the testing started. Therefore, it was very hard to predict how complex the testing would be in the end.

"Is that what this means? The arrow going back to this configure task?" Haffner asked.

"Yes, there is a decision here, right after the tests, and if all tests are fine we could package and ship the laser unit, but the default case is that we go back to the configuration task because the laser unit does not fit the specified test scenario."

"Oh my goodness," Haffner exclaimed. He threw up his hands in horror. "I knew it. I knew about the increased complexity of our lasers. I knew about the customer-specific test scenarios. But I never linked it to more test cycles. This, in combination with more complex test scenarios, is a nightmare."

The meeting room was silent. Only the fan of the projector could be heard. Haffner stared at the slide on the wall and was buried in thought again. Tom stood near the presentation computer and waited for a reaction from Haffner.

"Do you have an idea on how to fix it?," Haffner finally asked.

"The step itself is unavoidable," Tom started cautiously. "Maybe the way we do configuration and testing can be optimized so we will need less iterations."

Haffner nodded; he still had not taken his eyes off the slide.

"I'm not an engineer," Tom continued, "but it might be possible to define subunits which can be tested together before the complete laser unit is tested with all components."

Haffner turned away from the projection and looked at Tom. "From an engineering point of view," he explained, "it makes sense to test subunits first. But the people doing it are not the engineers."

Haffner stood up from his chair. He paced beside the conference table, staring at the carpet. Tom could see his brain working.

"Okay, Mr. Bauer. I think I need to discuss this with A.J. as soon as possible."

Tom turned off the projector and shut down the computer.

"Please send me your slides, Mr. Bauer. I liked that, with the high-level model and the different subprocesses. Quite a nice way to present the information."

Haffner was satisfied with Tom's presentation. He emphasized that the process models were indeed helpful to trace the story and to point at particular steps to discuss.

"What are you doing next week, Mr. Bauer?" Haffner suddenly asked, and, as Tom didn't answer, he continued, "I just made a deal. Quite a big project. We'll team up with PDO to deliver a very big machine. I already set up the basics with the head of PDO, but there are still some details to be discussed regarding the collaboration. You and your process skills should provide a good basis for making sure that we don't overlook any important details. To be more specific, I want you to identify all the documents we need to exchange with PDO. Ready for that?"

"I will do my best."

"I know."

Chapter 7

How to Interact with Business Partners

Tom checked his watch. It was a quarter past seven in the evening. He took a cab from the train station to the hotel, dropped off his bag, and took another cab to meet David in a bar. The first time David and Tom had met was when they studied together in Lancaster. They shared just a few classes, but they hung out a lot in their spare time. Tom found David again when he browsed his social network for process experts. It turned out that David became a B2B process consultant. Tom was not quite sure what that meant but arranged a meeting when he found out that David had a project in the same city where Tom had to go for the PDO job.

When Tom entered the bar he immediately recognized David. He wore a nice suit, and the silk tie properly completed the picture of a successful consultant. He must have come directly from work. They took a seat in the corner of the crowded bar and ordered two pints of draft beer. Things went very well after they graduated from the university, but it was hard to keep track of the individual careers. David worked for one of those large software companies selling software systems to even larger companies. He briefly described his job as a negotiation between different companies that want to work together. David had not changed much. He still talked a lot, and loved sharing anecdotes.

"Tell me about your new job," David finally asked. "What exactly are you doing?"

Tom told him about LaserTec and Haffner; that he had still not fully understood how a laser actually works; and that everyday life in the company is quite different from what he had expected it to be. He told David about Anne and how he was slowly becoming the process expert at work.

The word "process expert" triggered something in David: "So we basically do the same thing!"

"What do you mean?"

"Well, what I do all day long is look at processes and how they can be supported using software. My specialty is business-to-business integration, often related to supply chains and logistics. Especially in scenarios with a high number of interactions involved, automation really makes a difference. You would be amazed by how much money can be saved by exchanging electronic messages instead of good old faxes."

Tom thought about the piles of faxes at LaserTec and Anne looking at each of them, making colored annotations, and sticking post-its on them.

"Sounds great. How do you do this?" Tom wanted to know.

"As a start, we do the same thing as you do at LaserTec," David started explaining. "We first use process modeling techniques to capture all dependencies between the different interactions. Parallel to that, we define what content a message should have. As a next step we dive into the technical details and add concrete message specifications and some other technical configurations, regarding security, for example. Once the different partners have agreed on this, my colleagues take over and realize the processes using software systems. By the way, what modeling language are you using at LaserTec? Are you familiar with event-driven process chains?"

That didn't ring a bell for Tom. "No, we are using BPMN. Have you heard of it?"

"You must be kidding. I am the biggest fan of BPMN on this planet!" David burst out. "We use it extensively. My team tried different other techniques over the last years, but BPMN turned out to be the one that our customers accept best. They love the icons. And you have to agree that those little message symbols do look good."

Tom felt as if someone had switched off the lights. Was David really talking about the same language?

"What symbols?" he asked and took a big gulp of beer.

"I mean the event symbols. You haven't come across them yet?" David rummaged in his bag and finally pulled out a laptop. It's a hyper-fancy, ultra-light-weight, business-user-only laptop such as Tom had never seen before. David put his laptop on the table.

"Ah, there we go." The laptop came to life in zero time, showing the usual corporate desktop design for big companies. David opened his modeling tool. "You know about collapsed pools and message flow, right?"

"Collapsed pools? Collapsed subprocesses you mean."

"No. Pools! Empty pools. The process is hidden inside the pool."

Tom was confused. David sipped his beer. "Look. What I am drawing now is not exactly a process model. But let's get there step by step. Let me first get you up to speed with message flows. But you do know about sequence flow, don't you?"

"Of course, it is essential for the activity order within a process! "

"Alright, what you see here are two empty pools with message flow between them." Tom looked at the screen. He only saw two rectangles without text in them and a dashed line connecting them.

"Could we label this? That would help me to understand it better," Tom inquired.

"Sure. Let's take an example from LaserTec. Tell me, where do you interact with business partners?"

Tom immediately came up with the answer. "We are doing a joint project with another company. That's what I'm here for."

"Great! What's the company's name?" David was ready to type in the names.

"It's PDO. Don't ask me what it stands for."

"And what documents are you exchanging?"

"Hard question. The meeting is tomorrow. I had a short look at the documents on my train ride today. We must agree on project specific contracts. That's already for sure."

"So you are going to send them the contract and then they send a signed contract back?"

"I guess so. Also we will send them some kind of final report in the end."

"Too easy." David quickly completed the diagram. He turned his notebook toward Tom and ordered two more beers by waving his hand at the young lady behind the counter.

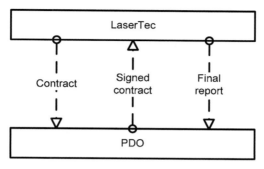

"Is that a BPMN diagram?" Tom mistrusted the model as it didn't show any familiar elements.

"Of course, it is," David assured him. "Here," he pointed at the rectangles, "you see two empty pools. Each one represents an organization, the companies. They have processes inside, but those processes aren't shown here. And the dashed lines denote the information exchanged between the organizations."

"Interesting...." Tom was lost in thought. "I have never seen any BPMN diagram with more than one pool." Tom paused. "And reading the diagram from left to right tells me that first the contract is sent, then the signed contract and the final report, doesn't it?"

"Not really," David replied. "This diagram does not tell you anything about the order of messages. All it says is that there are two organizations, LaserTec and PDO, and that they might exchange documents. It also tells you who sends a document to whom, and the direction of the information flow. But that's about it."

"Um, I am not quite convinced of this model. It might be useful to simply enumerate the documents involved. But without dependencies I don't really see the point."

"What additional information would you like to express?"

Tom thought for a while. "We work with PDO to produce special laser machines for our customers. I would like to express that LaserTec handles the contracting with PDO and the ultimate customer in parallel. And the final report can only be forwarded to PDO once it has arrived from the customer."

"So you want a third party involved – the customer," David said.

"Right. And we might also add that the signed contract can only be returned after the contract is sent. I mean this should be obvious, but we can include it anyway."

"Okay, okay. No Problem," David said and started modeling. This time it took him a bit longer. While he was still adding shapes, he explained, "You can combine message flow with sequence flow in the same diagram. The message flow shows who sends a document to whom. And the sequence flow shows the dependencies between the message exchanges within each partner." Tom observed David connecting different shapes.

"Please also include that the customer sends a hand-over certificate," Tom added. "For us, it is the sign that the machine is running properly at the customer side."

"That's a good point. Because the final report to PDO is probably sent after everything is set up and running?"

"Of course."

"In that case, the customer process is very simple: He first gets the contract, then he returns the signed document, and, finally, he sends the hand-over certificate. That's what you meant, right?"

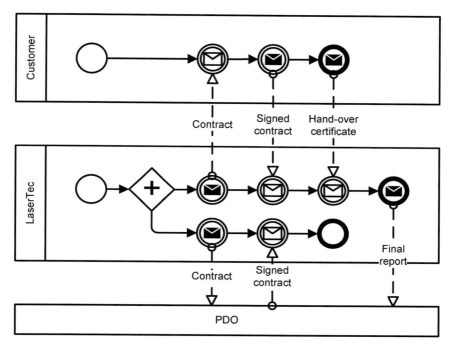

Tom took a look at the diagram and wondered, "I didn't know about events for sending or receiving information. I would have expected a simple task for that."

"Well, you can do that," David explained. He took a pen from his jacket and drew a sketch on the back of a napkin. "A task might also have incoming and outgoing message flow. Using events for sending and receiving is just an alternative way of depicting it. However, I would use an event only if it is about sending or receiving information. I would use a task if there is more work associated with it."

"I see," Tom inspected the drawing on the napkin. "It's a nice way of depicting it, with these black and white messages for sending and for receiving information."

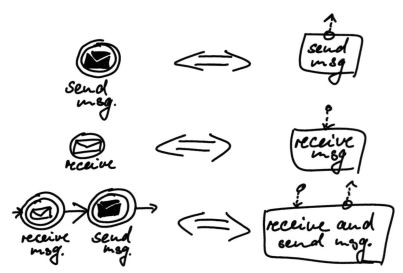

"Yeah, that's cool!" David answered. "I like this a lot. And it makes it much easier to read diagrams. With the different message symbols you can easily distinguish between inbound and outbound interactions. When the message symbol is white with black strokes, then the message is received. When the background and stroke color are inverted, then the message is sent. This color coding schema for catching and throwing events holds true also for other event types in BPMN."

"There are more types of events besides messages?"

"Oh, yes, there are. But the most important type is the message – at least for me, because they symbolize information exchange between business partners."

"I see," said Tom.

David continued, "By the way, you can add more BPMN elements to this model. But in this diagram type you usually want to focus on the interaction. Adding internal activities is then up to every partner. They do not have to reveal to others what they do internally."

"Sure, I get it. Companies even compete over processes," Tom concluded.

"You bet they do," David replied. "I'll take this," Tom said, folding the napkin and placing it into his pocket next to his small black book. "Can you also send me the link to the diagram?" he asked. "I think that is really what I needed."

"No problem at all. But will you have another beer with me?" David raised his glass.

"No problem at all," Tom replied. They chinked their glasses and emptied them.

It was 8:55 a.m. Tom was sitting in a meeting room at PDO. Tom was reviewing the process from last night when a man stepped in. He was in his early forties, and his badly shaved beard made him look a bit like an absentminded professor.

"Interesting challenge we got here," he started right away. "Hello. My name is Webber. Have you already checked out the requirements that General Vehicles sent over?"

"I quickly browsed through them on my way here," Tom replied.

Webber continued, "Let's hope for a smooth project with them this time."

"You have already developed machines for them?" Tom asked. He researched the basic facts about General Vehicles, a major supplier for the big car manufacturers, on the Internet. With the rise of catalytic converters they specialized in sophisticated exhaust pipe liners, and now they dominate the market.

"Well, back in the days when we developed components for their assembly line," Webber said as he took a seat next to Tom, "we developed our pipe liners for almost a half a year. Then political issues took over and they changed the supplier. In the end, I still don't know what went wrong. I'm an engineer. I don't deal with politics, I deal with projects."

"How about joint projects like this one? Have you done a lot of this kind?"

"Well," Webber took a deep breath, "too many, honestly. Sometimes I wish we were working on our own. But to get the big bites you have to team up. But coordination can be a nightmare. You know, the partners need to coordinate their work."

"And that's what we are here for," Tom said.

"I would be happy if we'd simply share the important documents," Webber explained, "synchronizing support plans, for example. And most important of all: Get prepared for emergencies. Things go wrong. Machines do break down." He paused. "You have to be prepared! "

"We just have to agree on what each partner has to do when, right?" Tom asked.

"That's easier said than done," Webber replied, "I always try to write it down and share the documents. But nobody looks at them. People don't like to work their way through lengthy texts. And if they do, they misinterpret it for their own ends."

"At LaserTec we started capturing our activities in process models," Tom explained. "That way, we get a clear description of the responsibilities. The visual diagrams seem to help when discussing the processes with the people involved. The goal is to generate a common understanding, but most important, when discussing we can point at steps within the big picture to ensure everybody is on the same page."

"Um, that sounds valuable. I have never seen such diagrams. Can you show me an example?" Webber was intrigued.

Tom didn't have any printed diagrams with him. But he had the models sent by David this morning. He invited Webber to look at his notebook screen.

"Look," Tom started explaining, "here is PDO and here is LaserTec. And the customer is General Vehicle. You can see now how the parties interact and what messages they exchange."

"Alright, alright," Webber said, and, with a glance at the screen, he asked, "Can you please start by explaining the elements and what they mean?"

Tom took a big step back and started explaining about pools as organizations, about dotted lines for information exchange and different message symbols for incoming and outgoing messages. Webber asked questions about the meaning of the AND gateway and then refocused away from the notation to the actual content. By pointing at the elements in the model, Webber and Tom found a basis for their work. They discussed the scenario and changed the diagram. Meanwhile, Webber recalled even more details that had to be considered.

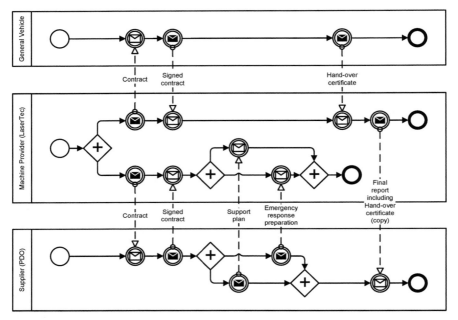

"Mr. Webber, can I talk to you for a minute?" An elder man had entered the room with a serious look on his face. Webber apologized and followed the man.

Tom used the opportunity to rearrange the shapes a bit, trying to have as few lines crossing each other as possible. Tom found an automatic layout function in his tool. But as the layout result looked worse than what he came up with himself, he undid it quickly.

A couple of minutes later, Webber was back in the room. His face was pale. Obviously, the old man had given him a hard time.

"Sorry about that," Webber said and took a seat.

"No problem. Your boss?" Tom was curious.

"Yes. There is this project," he started. "I need to leave you for a while. I suggest we spend just a little more time now, and continue after lunch. My apologies."

"Don't worry, I'll be fine," Tom replied. He didn't dare to ask for more details.

Webber left again, and a couple of minutes later he returned with a slight smile on his face. "Here we go," he said, taking the seat next to Tom who started discussing the diagram on his computer screen. But Tom knew that Webber's thoughts were elsewhere. So, he quickly wrapped up the discussion by going through the model.

"I think we should specify them in greater detail," Webber said.

"What do you mean?" Tom asked.

"The preparation for emergencies and the support plan." Webber circled them with his finger on the screen. "We should note down what these documents are about. I can show you some old ones and we can work out a template. It's important that they follow a common structure and contain certain information. I always thought that this was common sense, but I can show you funny counter examples."

They reviewed old documents and discussed a good structure for a template. From time to time, Webber glanced at the diagram. Then he pointed at parts to underline his arguments.

"Could you actually reflect in the model that these documents typically don't come in on time?" Webber finally asked. "It sometimes requires several reminders."

"Uh, interesting." Tom thought for a moment. He pushed away the templates and focused on the diagram. "How do you decide that a reminder is necessary?"

"It's a matter of time," Webber explained. "After a week I should definitely contact the partner and kindly ask them for the documents again. And the second reminder won't be as nice as the first one." Webber checked his watch and then turned to Tom again, "Speaking of time, I fear I have to leave now. But before I forget it, there could also be the case that the documents are simply incomplete. This would require us to ask for a more complete version. This is important, so I'd like to see that documented in the process as well. If that is possible at all."

Webber apologized once again and headed off. Tom took the chance to catch some fresh air. Webber's requirements about time and distinguishing different message contents really bothered Tom. Probably, David would know how to do it. Tom called him.

David was happy to help Tom although he was heading for a meeting. He offered to email Tom a slide set on loops in BPMN. Tom was not sure whether loops would be helpful in this situation. But David had no time to explain. Tom decided to go for lunch first. After lunch, he took a long walk along the river before returning to PDO and checked his emails.

As promised, David had sent him a slide set. But it only contained one slide and not much additional information. He only stated in his email that loops are a challenge especially when they affect different pools. The diagram contained small examples for different kinds of loops. The only example that seemed familiar to Tom was the one containing a subprocess with a loop marker. The diagram said, "I choose to do another iteration."

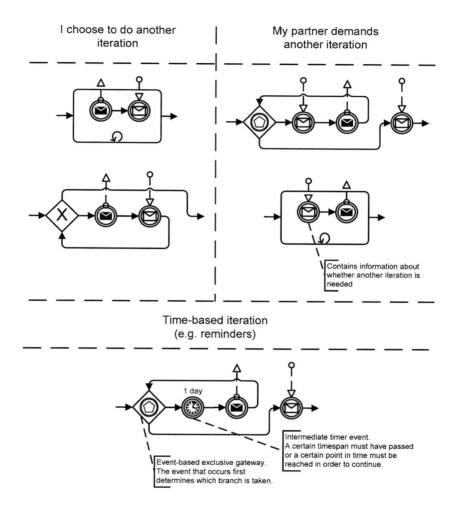

I choose to do another iteration

My partner demands another iteration

Time-based iteration (e.g. reminders)

Contains information about whether another iteration is needed

Intermediate timer event. A certain timespan must have passed or a certain point in time must be reached in order to continue.

Event-based exclusive gateway. The event that occurs first determines which branch is taken.

"Um, that's interesting," Tom mumbled to himself. He knew from Anne that the loop marker could be seen as macro for using XOR gateways and cycles of sequence flow. Here again, this was illustrated in the same column of the diagram. An XOR gateway split the sequence flow at the point where the decision was made about whether another iteration was necessary. Interestingly, the same XOR gateway merged the sequence flow again. Tom had never seen this. He would have used separate XOR gateways for splitting and joining the flow. "Yet another shortcut to do it with the same gateway," he concluded.

There was one shape Tom had not seen before. Some kind of gateway, he could deduce from the diamond shape, but the symbol contained in the gateway shape was new to him. It appeared twice in the diagram, and in both cases it was followed by intermediate events. David added a small text annotation to one of the gateways "event-based exclusive gateway," it said. Tom remembered that the full name for XOR gateways was "data-based exclusive gateway." As the name only differed by one word, this new gateway must be somehow similar to the XOR gateway he had already applied so often.

Tom read on, "The event that occurs first determines which branch is taken." In the case of an XOR gateway, Tom recalled, it was also the case that exactly one branch was to be taken. However, for the XOR gateway, it was not an event determining which branch, but, rather, conditions that were either true or false for the "data" of the process, Tom concluded. Therefore, the term data-based gateway now made sense to him.

The shape with a timer symbol was also new to Tom. He immediately understood that it was an intermediate event by simply looking at the two circles. The text annotation that David added was again self-explanatory.

Webber wanted reminders to be included in the diagrams. That was exactly what the intermediate timer event was good for. But it should only be triggered if the documents do not arrive on time. According to the samples provided by David, that was what could be expressed using the new gateway type. It was like a race. The event that happened first determined which path was taken.

Tom couldn't wait to start modeling again. But as he took a look at the document he recognized that the new model was going to be much larger, considering that he needed to introduce the reminder loop twice into the model. As Anne had told him, a diagram for communication should fit one page. But how?

He searched the Web for a BPMN solution to slice models, and found a Web page with "Link events – mostly used as off-page connectors, allows for the partitioning of a large diagram into several smaller ones." Further down on the same page he discovered, "A link event is either of catching or of throwing nature. Link events should occur in pairs: A throwing link event in one diagram points to a catching link event in another diagram. If both have the same name then the two link events combined are interpreted as a sequence flow."

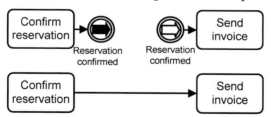

The description was illustrated with a sample. These link events seemed to be useful. Tom remembered the hint from David last night, that there are different BPMN event types but they followed a similar color coding pattern. Tom started modeling by creating a new diagram. He put in a pool for the machine provider and a collapsed pool for the supplier. He started his process model with a catching intermediate link event. The arrow was white. The stroke was black. That fit the scheme and would be triggered if the complementary event with the same name was reached. He named it, "Wait for support plan." He also put a throwing intermediate link event with the same name in the process just where the support plan was expected by the customer. That would redirect the sequence flow to his little process. To link back, he put a throwing intermediate link event at the end of his new diagram and named it "Complete support plan arrived."

Tom included an event-based gateway and an intermediate timer event as was shown in David's document. That would capture the timeout. But something was still missing. Webber wanted to distinguish between incomplete documents and complete documents. In case a document was incomplete, a revised version must be requested. Tom still had no clue how to model this properly.

He searched the Web again, but couldn't find any hint. He finally decided to send a text message to David:

```
Hey David, thanks again for the diagram. But
how to model a branch that is chosen depending
on whether an incoming document is complete or
not? Thx, Tom
```

David responded in less than a minute:

```
Either you use one message event + XOR gateway,
or more elegantly: use an event-based gateway +
two message events, one for complete, one for
incomplete.
Have fun, Dave
```

Tom could have come up with the first solution with the XOR gateway, but the alternative was more appealing, indeed. There already was an event-based gateway in the model, so another message event didn't add too much additional complexity.

While Tom was finishing up the diagram, Mr. Webber stepped into the room again.

"I hope you were able to use your time productively." Webber was a lot more at ease and relaxed than he had been in the morning. "Ah, you have continued working on the interaction models?"

"Yes, it was quite challenging to factor in all the additional requirements you put up," Tom started. "But it's done now. Do you want to have a look at the models?"

"Sure." Webber moved his chair over to Tom to have a better view of the laptop screen.

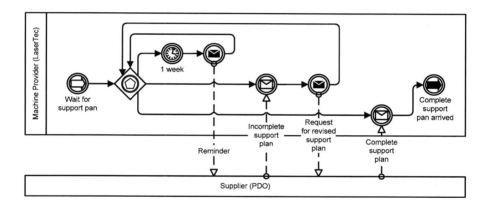

Tom showed him the diagram and started explaining, "First of all, I cut out the process part that we want to focus on."

"Where is the rest? Did you throw it away?"

"No, no. I just concentrate on a part of the model that we are most interested in. The events with the arrows in the middle." Tom pointed at the link events, "They connect this diagram to the original model."

"Okay," Webber said, but didn't sound totally convinced. "And how does that work?"

"They are counterparts of these events with the same name in the other model." Tom showed Webber the link events that he introduced in the original model.

"I see the encircled arrows with the same name are the gluing points."

"Exactly. But let's focus on this part here." Tom pointed at his new reminder model.

Webber took a look at the diagram, "Is that a clock?"

"Yes," Tom responded, "This is a timer event. It is set to one week, so if no support plan arrives then we go this way and send a reminder."

"I see; it's a timer. When does it start running?"

Tom was not totally sure. For a second, he thought of asking David, but he didn't have to, because all of a sudden, it all made sense.

"We start it whenever we arrive here." Tom pointed at the event-based gateway.

"That looks complicated. What does it mean?"

"It means that we wait for something to happen. We set the timer and wait for one of the next events to occur. Then, either a complete or incomplete support plan arrives, or the week is over. But we wait."

"Yeah," Webber said with a smile on his face, "that's exactly what we do." They both paused for a second before Webber broke the silence. "Okay, just to get the complete picture. Three things can happen: If I don't receive anything within one week, I send a reminder." Webber followed the sequence flow with his finger while talking. "If I receive an incomplete one, I ask them for a revised version...."

"Or you get the complete support plan, and then you're done," said Tom.

"I got it, but...," Webber frowned.

"What is bothering you?" Tom asked.

"I like the diagrams; I think they are a valuable tool to communicate knowledge. Actually, I want everybody at PDO to read them and to work accordingly. But how can I ensure that everybody understands them?"

"I know what you mean." Tom assured Webber: "First of all, you should add a legend to each diagram. Also you might set up a workshop to present the models, and you will need additional textual documentation to go with it."

"Yes, a workshop or some kind of training would be good," Webber said. "Have you attended a training to learn all this?"

"No, but I had good teachers," Tom replied.

"And you became a good teacher yourself. Could you teach my people to do the same thing?"

"Well, I'm not at that stage yet. But I can document today's findings and share them with you. I will explain the findings textually, and we will use the models to support the message."

"That's a good idea."

They went on to discuss the details of their further collaboration. When Tom left for the train, Webber thanked Tom again for the productive meeting. Still, it bothered Tom that he obviously did not have the full language standard and all its elements in hand. If David had not been there to help him, he could not have done it. He decided to look for professional BPMN training to help him master the whole language set. While still on the train, he wrote an email to Haffner.

```
Dear Mr. Haffner,

The meeting with PDO was a good start. We
agreed on the most important documents to be
exchanged.

It turned out that BPMN is also suited to cap-
ture how business partners interact.

To enhance my modeling skills I'd like to at-
tend a professional BPMN training.

Regards,

Tom
```

Afterward, Tom prepared some slides to sum up the meeting for Haffner. When his laptop battery ran out, he leaned back and watched the countryside fly by. Somewhere along the line he searched his pockets for a tissue and ended up holding a napkin in his hands. Scribbled on it were different ways to model interactions, alternatively using events or tasks. He recalled that David drew on the napkin when they sat together in the bar. Maybe it was time to sum up all the BPMN lessons he had learned on this business trip. He took out his notebook and started noting things down.

Empty Pool

Represents a business partner. It's used when the internals of the pool are not known or not of interest for a model.

Message Flow

Denotes where information flows across organizational boundaries. Sequence flow connects activities within the same pool. Message flow connects different pools and activities from different pools.

Intermediate Message Send Event

A message is sent to another organization. If additional effort is required, e.g., to create the content for the message, then a sending task might be used instead.

Intermediate Message Receive Event

A message comes in. The sequence flow pauses until the message is received.

End Message Send Event

A message is sent to another organization as the result of the process.

Message Send Activity

Similar to a message send event. However, here we assume that something must be done before the message can actually be sent. E.g., a quote needs to be created before it is sent.

Message Receive Activity
Similar to a message receive event. Again, the receive activity does more: After receiving the message, something else happens in this step.

Message Send/Receive Activity
Tasks can be used to send and receive messages or vice versa. Here, a message is sent and a response is waited for.

Event-based Exclusive Gateway
One branch is taken based on which event occurs first. Often there is a choice between different messages or between messages and timeouts.

Intermediate Timer Event
Represents waiting for a certain delay to be over or for a certain point in time to arrive.

Intermediate Link Events (Throwing/Catching)
Link events are off-page connectors. They are useful for partitioning large process models into manageable pieces. One throwing link event corresponds to a catching link event in another diagram. A pair of link events is equivalent to a sequence flow.

Chapter 8

The Pioneer

Tom hadn't expected Haffner to send him to the training right away. But Tom was able to book a well-recognized training class just two weeks after his trip to PDO. On the first day of training, Tom got up early, took a shower, and headed for the breakfast room of the hotel where the training was being held. On his way he browsed the agenda for today's class, which was posted in the lobby. It started at 8:30 a.m. The breakfast buffet looked delicious. Tom took a seat near the window and enjoyed his cold orange juice and the view overlooking a park. The sun rose, flocks of birds were in the trees. It was a very calm morning.

"Hi, I am Linda," announced a middle-aged lady with modern frameless glasses, a beige business outfit, and a shrill voice that terminated any daydreams. "May I join you?"

"Ahh, sure, why not?" Tom tried to be polite, feeling somewhat overwhelmed by the lady.

"The answer isn't why not, but why yes!" Linda remarked.

"So, why yes?" Tom tried to challenge her.

"Because I am in charge of process engineering at Mobtel, one of the largest telecommunication providers in the country. I saw you checking today's agenda," Linda explained. "But I'm so excited to attend the training by Charles Timber himself. He is a pioneer in business process modeling and a guru on BPMN."

"Is that so? In fact, you were right. I am attending the class. Tom of LaserTec, pleased to meet you."

"The pleasure is mine," said Linda. She took a sip of tea before she continued, "We at Mobtel have just started a massive process innovation effort. The goal is to model all processes we have, to optimize them, and finally to automate them to make them fast and less costly. Huge budget involved."

"Interesting," Tom said while chewing his cereal.

"We have millions of customers, you know. And six months ago we started to model the processes. But now we want to change to BPMN as the modeling notation."

Tom looked up from his breakfast and asked, "If not BPMN, what did you use before?"

"EPCs! Do you know them?" Linda asked.

"No, what does it mean?"

"Event-driven process chains. It's a notation to capture processes. But we ended up with huge process models, and they were hard to read," Linda explained. "The IT department, especially, wanted to change to BPMN. They have to read the models we create, and they think BPMN will be more compact, readable, and precise."

"And what do you think?" Tom asked.

"I have heard that BPMN is much more expressive. And at the same time so easy to learn. Everybody can do it."

"I don't know this EPC stuff, but, after all, BPMN is just another modeling language. In any case, I think you need dedicated people to do it."

Linda was quiet for a moment. Tom could see her brain working. He enjoyed the moment of silence and went to get more food from the buffet.

He wondered why Linda hadn't asked him for his background and his motivation for attending the class, but he was fine with the situation. For a while, both ate quietly. Tom watched the birds in the park and again started enjoying the calm morning.

"I have to leave now," Linda suddenly broke the silence. "I'll see you in the training class."

Half an hour later, Tom sat in an air-conditioned room of the hotel, with two dozens of his fellow students. Charles entered the room. He was in his early sixties with tanned skin and wore a dark suit, matching tie, and a golden watch.

An assistant set up the presentation equipment while Charles welcomed his students. "Good morning. My name is Charles Timber. I am happy to have you here!"

The assistant distributed the training materials, and Charles started the class. "Business process management is the road to success. Every day new companies set up process modeling efforts to understand how they operate and to have the chance to improve their business. And BPMN is on its way to becoming the standard process modeling notation, so, congratulations, dear friends, this is the right training to take!"

After a short pause, he continued, "But beware. BPMN cannot do miracles. In BPMN you can easily create models that nobody understands. So you need training. With the projects you do, you will gather experience that will make you a good process modeler. You will need to have a clear understanding of the people who will read your diagrams. But we will come to that later."

Charles asked for a brief round of introductions. It was quite a diverse group, with people from the financial sector, manufacturing, telecommunications, and public administration. Since there were novices to BPMN, Charles started with the basic material.

So I can daydream a little, Tom thought, as Charles explained activities, events, gateways, connecting objects, and data objects.

The day flew by. In the afternoon session, Charles talked about message and timer events, interacting processes, subprocesses, and more of the not-so-basic stuff. Charles added anecdotes here and there, which made the training quite entertaining. But, still, Tom didn't learn new language concepts. Maybe this was not such a good idea after all, Tom thought. At least there was the dinner that night, a social event that might bring more to the table than enjoyable food.

They met at a Japanese restaurant close by the hotel. Tom had never been to a Japanese restaurant before. Charles welcomed his students to the workshop dinner, and asked if soup, sushi, and an assortment of fried vegetables and seafood were fine for everybody. The attendees nodded. Some of them seemed to be happy that Charles would do the ordering. Charles waved over the waiter, "Konbanwa. We'll have Miso soup as a starter. As the main dish, please bring us a selection of Sushi, you know, Maki Sushi, Nigiri Sushi, and Sashimi. And also Tempura, for those of you who may prefer that."

Tom was impressed. Charles probably could have done the same

128

in a Portuguese, French, or Ethiopian restaurant, Tom thought.

"Anything to drink? ," the waiter asked.

"Japanese beer goes well with Sushi," Charles proposed, and heard no objections. "Do you have any idea what it takes to bring fresh sushi on this table?" Charles asked the group. "Processes! Many of them! Supply chains all over the place, processes that interact with each other. Out of Tuna? Find an alternative supplier! Be fast. Be on time. You won't eat old fish, will you?" Charles looked at his students, who hung on every word. So he continued, while the drinks arrived.

"You know, today we have learned how to model processes, the basic material. Tomorrow we look at the more exciting stuff. The out-of-Tuna-scenario, for instance. How you model things that you do not like to see happen. But, for now, let's enjoy the evening." Charles raised his glass, as did the others, enjoying the cold beer.

The group had a good time. They talked about their companies, what their goals in process management were. Linda even found a fellow student willing to discuss Mobtel's process strategies in detail. Tom learned that most of the students were in a position similar to his. They have tried to understand and to communicate how their companies work, and what can be improved. One young lady, sitting next to Tom, attracted his attention in particular. She was smart and when she started talking, everyone turned their attention to her. "I work for an insurance company. My job is overseeing the architecture of our information systems. It's quite a zoo. The IT landscape has grown over thirty years, and we struggle to satisfy user requirements," she explained.

"What does this have to do with your processes?" somebody asked.

"Well, the idea is to use processes to represent how the different information systems work together," the young lady explained.

"Still, I don't get it," Tom entered the conversation. "We at LaserTec use processes to communicate how people work. You know, the departments that are involved, ordering of activities, and things like this. We want to understand and improve that."

"Oh, what we do is actually quite similar," the lady responded. "We use processes to show how our systems cooperate and how we can improve that. This is much better than discussing systems integration on the code level."

"So, like us," Tom added, "you use process modeling as a visual means by which different domain experts can communicate a complex topic."

"Right, Tom" Charles entered the discussion. "The IT guys have a hard time catching up with fast changing requirements. They need to make a rusty old truck look like a shiny sports car!"

"Exactly." The young lady was the only one who understood Charles' words. "Our rusty old truck is the dozens of software systems that have been around for decades, and the shiny sports car is the Web application that our clients use to access our systems."

"The Web has changed everything." Charles caught the drift. "Suddenly users see right into your information systems and they immediately see if they are a mess."

"Can you give an example?" Tom asked.

"Sure. Assume you use a Web application to change your address information, or you marry and take the last name of your spouse. This application sits on top of some old database application, and your changes somehow make their way into the database."

"I see, but so far things are fine," Tom remarked.

"Yes, but this is only half of the story. If customer data are also stored, in another system, like a dedicated customer management system, then things become tricky."

"Why so?" Tom had little knowledge of IT architectures, but he could follow Charles' explanation.

"If the change is only done in the one database system and not in the customer system, then you have inconsistent data. One entity of the real world – you – and two different last names. Not good."

The young lady took up the thread of the discussion. "This actually happened to us once. We sent out a mailing to our clients informing them about a new product. Some client addresses were incorrect. So the letter came back. Not very nice."

"Did you have last name changes?" somebody asked.

"Yes, quite a few. If you have a few million customers, you have many changes. Every day. This is why we tried to automate the process in the first place," the lady continued.

"But if some customers do not get a promotional mailing, what's the problem?" Tom asked.

"Well, promotional campaigns and annoyed customers are one thing, but sending out documents that are of legal importance is another. If the documents are returned simply because your address data is inconsistent, and you miss a certain deadline as a consequence – that is where it stops being funny."

"So, due to your lack of IT integration, you had immediate effects on the business," Charles summarized. "Process modeling is not magic, but it helps identifying those issues."

"Yes, and if there is a change-address activity in the database system, then there must be a change-address activity in the customer system," the lady concluded.

The food came; they all enjoyed the Miso soup and the Sushi. Tom was a bit reluctant to try the Sushi, but he finally did. He liked it with a bit of ginger. But his eyes filled with tears from the Wasabi.

After dinner, Charles proposed to go to a bar for a few drinks, but most people excused themselves and went back to the hotel. Tom was eager to join him. He wanted to hear more stories from other people and how they use BPMN. When they left the restaurant he heard Linda's voice. "Wait for me, I'll be right with you!" They went to a bar right next to the hotel. The men ordered beer, and the ladies, cocktails. They took a table right next to the stage, where a guy with worn out jeans played his guitar. Nice tune, Tom thought.

Linda opened the conversation, "Charles, may I ask you a question? How long have you been doing these courses?"

"Oh, I have been giving courses all my life. Actually I have been a university lecturer."

"So you taught process management?" Tom asked.

"The story is a bit more complicated. I studied sociology and political science. I even taught these topics at the university. But then I got divorced, you know, so I was ready for a change."

Charles took a big gulp of beer. "I always liked to work with people, to communicate. So I entered the organizational development department of a large insurance company," and, looking at the young lady, "your competition. This was back in the early nineties, when process modeling became a hot topic. The Hammer and Champy book."

"You mean *Re-Engineering the Corporation*," the lady responded.

"Right. The book has a number of stories about how companies used a process-oriented perspective to reduce cost or to improve customer satisfaction, lower processing times, and things like that," Charles continued.

"Hammer and Champy proposed a radical re-design of processes," the lady threw in.

"They did, but that didn't work out in many cases. As a sociologist, I can tell you, when people are involved. People don't like radical change. If you are on your own, change whatever you like, fine. But if your processes have people involved, then evolutionary changes are the way to go."

"Yes, evolution works quite well, and, after all, it brought us here," Tom tried to look intelligent. "But even in evolution sometimes there is a radical step. Some kind of quantum leap."

"Good point, Tom," Charles began to enjoy the conversation. "Yes, I guess the point is to change the really important things radically and to strongly support such quantum-leap changes. Other changes should go step by step, so that you do not lose your people."

"It must have been around that time," the lady came back to the point, "when workflow was a hot topic. I was still in school then, but my company burned a lot of money with workflow solutions that never worked out as planned. It must have been around the middle or end of the nineties."

"Yes, there was a lot of workflow hype," Charles remembered. "The problem was that the workflow guys did not read the Hammer and Champy book in detail."

"Well, the book started the process management hype, so they must have read it," Tom interjected.

"One of the ideas of Hammer and Champy is that you can speed up processes by reducing hand-overs," Charles explained. "Activities with the same context should be assigned to the same person. Let me give you an example. Assume you have an insurance claim. You need to check if the case is handled by the policy of the client, you have to invite reviewers, you have to make a decision, and you finally have to inform the client about the outcome. With workflow technology you can easily create four activities – check, invite reviews, decide, and send the letter. No more idle times, documents are forwarded automatically between the workers, all very nice. And since workflow does all this work allocation and role resolution, it is easy to select different people for these activities."

"But each person needs to make himself familiar with the case," Tom added.

"Exactly! This is why you have the nice workflow solution, but still people are the bottleneck," Charles responded. "IT support for processes is essential, indeed. But you need to consider carefully where IT really helps. In this insurance example the most important thing is to separate the routine cases from the complex cases. The routine cases can be handled by a generalist or even be automated completely. The special cases are delegated to a specialist."

"So it's about using resources efficiently, right?" Tom asked.

"You are absolutely right, Tom." Charles was happy to see his student learn. "Software systems are very good for doing highly repetitive tasks. But remember: Implementation or configuration of these systems does not come for free! You have to calculate how much the introduction of such a system costs in comparison to doing tasks manually. And the same holds true for process coordination."

"Process coordination?" Tom asked again.

Charles replied, "Somebody has to ensure the flow of work, and there are again many different alternatives for accomplishing work tasks. Imagine that the person carrying out one activity triggers the person that is responsible for the next activity. Or you have somebody doing this triggering without actually being involved in the activities. And, in the extreme case, a software system takes care of the triggering and pushing work into the inboxes of people – which is exactly what workflow systems do."

Charles noticed that the discussion was getting too technical, and it had been a long day for the students, so he wrapped up. "I guess that workflow technology in those days was a bit too technology-driven; the overall context of the process and the people were left behind. But the modern process notations, including BPMN, are very much inspired by the workflow languages. We'll come back to that tomorrow."

It was ten to midnight and the ladies excused themselves to return to the hotel. The others left with them. Only Charles and Tom were the last ones standing.

"Go for another beer, Tom?" Charles proposed.

"Okay, one last one."

Charles waved the waiter over, who a short time later returned with two beers.

"May I come back to this workflow thing?" Tom asked.

"Sure."

"Um," Tom was not sure where to start. "So, workflow is not only the technical stuff, but also process modeling? And then it is also about the 'work flow,' the flow of work in the organization?"

"Workflow is some kind of a chameleon beast," Charles responded. "You start with process modeling, because you need to know how your organization works. Our nice business process diagrams represent work that is performed in the organization – what people do in their work. Day in, day out. You focus on how the work of John relates to the work of Anne. And that of Anne to that of Pete. And so on. Process models show you how the work flows from John to Anne and further down to Pete!"

"Okay, but it is not limited to one company, right?" Tom wanted to keep him going.

"Well, workflow is some kind of a local thing. You can ask what's your workflow? And the people in an organization will tell you. Interaction between companies, you were aiming at, is another thing. I would say the workflows of the companies involved communicate by messages. So it's individual workflows interacting with each other. In today's more advanced ideas of Business Process Management, or BPM, it's the end-to-end process that spans companies that goes center stage."

"In fact, the biggest thing to hit the process scene since 1993 was Smith and Fingar's *Business Process Management: The Third Wave.* Their

136

seminal book appeared 10 years after Hammer and Champy, and included a chapter called 'Reengineering Reengineering' that sorted out the problems and solutions to the radical 'rip and replace' approach of Hammer and Champy's reengineering. They also explained why workflow wasn't enough for complete process management. Their main point was that processes should be built, not to last, but built for change! Unlike the reengineering days where processes were 'cast in concrete' in enterprise systems known as enterprise resource planning or ERP systems, 'agility' is all in the Third Wave. Interestingly, Howard Smith was in the same job at the same company Champy had been in ten years earlier, and was co-founder of the BPMI.org, where BPMN was first created."

"That's all very interesting. It helps me to organize the buzz around BPM," Tom added.

Charles continued, "Yet, if you talk to three people you get four different definitions of BPM. The academic BPM people use formal models to describe processes. They even show mathematical properties of processes."

"Interesting, but does it help my company?" Tom wanted to know.

"It does. But first you have to know that in order to show these properties, there is a price to pay. And that price is abstraction." Charles entered telling mode.

"Similar to abstraction of real world processes to process models?" Tom gave it a try.

"Kind of similar. They abstract work activities to, guess what?"

"Um, to labels and text describing what needs to be done," Tom responded.

"Next guess?"

"Tell me! "

"Letters! They use letters to represent work! Here happens an A, then a B is done. Then either a C or D. But not both! How do you decide on C or D? Guess what?"

"They use conditions that are evaluated, either go this way or go that way?" Tom was happy to get this one.

"Nope. Random – they call it non-determinism. Either this or that. No conditions, not even data." said Charles.

"Okay, I see – then this mathematical stuff is complete garbage!" Tom seemed to understand.

"Far from it!" Charles surprised Tom. "You can only get these properties if you do these abstractions. And somehow they are right. In each branch you go either this way or that way. No more options! So these abstractions hold!"

"I see." Tom was lost. "But what can actually be shown?"

"Well, you can show that each process finally reaches the end, and if it does so, there is no activity left in the process."

"But what hinders a process from reaching its end?" Tom asked.

"Wrong synchronization. Assume you have an XOR split and an AND join." Charles made a brief sketch on a beer coaster.

"Okay," Tom saw the point, "exactly one branch is taken by the

XOR split. This branch finally reaches the AND join, but the AND join will wait for the next branch to finish."

"For how long does it wait?" Charles wanted to see that Tom got the point.

"Forever! The process is really stuck!" Tom answered.

"See, so this is why analysis of process models is such a very nice thing called *soundness*." Charles concluded.

Tom really enjoyed the conversation with Charles and finally asked, "I reckon it is quite an exhausting job teaching all this stuff."

"Sure, but if you like to communicate and work with people there are few jobs that give you higher job satisfaction," Charles responded.

"But isn't this getting boring?" Tom asked.

"Well, training is just half of what I am doing. I also coach projects. Sure, a lot of traveling, but every project is different. And people are always involved. Sometimes really deeply involved," Charles said.

"Yes, I have also had the experience that some people are very much involved, while others just don't seem to care," Tom replied.

"Well, you will learn that whenever it makes a difference to their work status and responsibilities, people do care. Once you come up with the processes of an organization, deficiencies pop up immediately. And often individual people are responsible for them. Or at least they base their status on the inefficiencies of the process. You know, large head-count and things like that," Charles explained.

"Actually, we at LaserTec are very excited about process management, even my boss," Tom said.

139

"Good to hear this, Tom," Charles replied. "I hope I was able to teach you something today."

"Actually, I am already familiar with most of the concepts you introduced today. But tomorrow there will surely be much more."

"Yes, we address advanced concepts like transactions, compensation. You know?" Charles waited for a reaction but didn't get any, so he continued, "Transactions are atomic units of work that are either completely executed or not at all."

"Appears to be a quite natural concept in business applications," Tom replied.

"Yes, but nevertheless very complex."

"Why?"

"Why? Because business activities take a long time, so that technical ways to ensure transactional behavior are more or less useless.

"What are those technical ways?" Tom got interested in the topic.

"Transactions have been developed in the context of database systems. The idea is that every database program should appear as if it was executed on its own and doesn't fail," Charles explained.

"So what's the point?" Tom took a gulp of beer.

"In large applications, you have hundreds of people and systems issuing database commands. So there's no single user environment whatsoever. To shield the application from the negative effects of multiple users and system failures, database systems feature a transaction processing component. These components are based on locking and logging. Locked data items prevent others from accessing them.

Logging data is what you do in case the system fails, in which case you can re-install the database to a consistent state," Charles explained.

"Okay, okay, I see." Tom was completely lost.

"Unfortunately, this all does not work in business activities. No way to roll back what you have done. You need compensation of activities that shouldn't have been executed. They do some kind of undoing of what was done before."

"And you can model this in BPMN?" Tom asked.

"You will see tomorrow."

Chapter 9

An Exceptional Lesson

"Welcome to today's agenda." Charles pointed at three key words he had written on the flipchart. He slowly read them out loud. "First, we are going to look at exceptions. An essential part of BPMN. Next: transactions. Then, after the break, I have planned a practice session. You will come up with models yourself, and we discuss them with the whole group. How does that sound?"

Nobody felt the need to comment on the agenda. Some of the students simply nodded their heads.

"The practical session is an excellent idea!" Linda said. "I am already excited about sharing my process models with the others!"

"Great to hear! I'm very excited about what you are going to share with us, Linda," Charles responded. "But let's get right into exception handling."

Tom wondered if there was a Linda in every class. Probably so.

"What are we actually capturing in our BPMN diagrams? We are interested in describing end-to-end processes, right? End-to-end meaning that we include the whole chain of value creation. From the initial input to the final output of the process. Input comes from the customer, output goes to the customer. Get the order, send the product." The class was spellbound. "And in BPMN we focus on the activities that are needed to create this value. On the flow of work, on the organizational breakdown of work, the assignment of decisions, and on the artifacts being produced on the way." Charles used big gestures during his monologue. He would probably have made for a good actor or a politician, Tom thought.

"Yesterday I talked briefly about sales processes. We considered them from end to end: From the very first contact with a customer until signing the deal, the creation of a sales order. We have seen that many different activities are needed. Such as calling the customer, retrieving information about potential sales volumes, carrying out proof-of-concepts, creation of quotes, and finally closing the deal. We have seen that many people are involved. The call center agent taking care of the first contact. Sales representatives doing most of the work. Pre-sales consultants for the proof-of-concept. Sales managers for quote approvals. Finally, there are different artifacts, as we learned: The customer information, the standard price list, the terms and conditions, the quote template, the actual quote, and then, finally, the sales order."

Charles paused for a moment and verified that everyone was still with him. He was happy to see that all his students were eager to hear how the story would evolve.

"Let's quickly draw the corresponding BPMN diagram. What would be a good way to do it?"

"Let's first draw the lanes," Linda scored first.

"Good idea, Linda." Charles sketched the lanes on the flipchart and labeled them with the abbreviations "Rep" for sales representative, "Mngr" for sales manager and "CC" for call center agent. Obviously, he ignored the pre-sales part of the process.

"Tom, what do I add next?" All heads turned toward Tom. It was a good thing that he had actually paid attention.

"We add the activities from left to right," Tom responded. "We should also integrate the order of activities, ah…um…the sequence flows, I mean."

"Very good, Tom." Charles still had the pen in his hand. He now added the tasks "Contact customer," "Negotiate conditions," "Create quote," "Approve quote," and "Close deal." He already had placed them in the corresponding lanes, indicating that the call center agent would contact the customer, the sales manager would approve the quote, and the sales representative would do all the rest.

"Alright." Charles quickly added the sequence flow arrows between the tasks. "I will only show the customer information, the quote, and the sales order for the moment. Just for the sake of simplicity." He finished the diagram and stepped to the side so that everybody could see it.

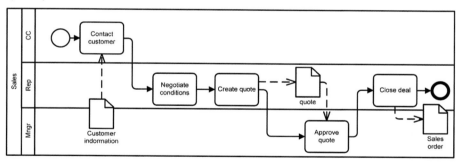

"What's the problem with this model?" Charles finally asked. "Any ideas?"

The students in the back row leaned forward a little bit to read the labels. Charles waited for a reaction. After a short pause, Tom suggested, "The model is very high level. It hides a lot of the important details."

"Important details?" Charles asked.

"Well, you didn't include the remaining data objects," Tom continued his answer. "Pre-sales does not appear, either. And, of course, there are many more activities in a sales process that are not reflected here."

"Okay, good points," Charles said patiently. "What about the sequence flow? Anything strange with that?"

"Um, on that level I could imagine that a quote is not approved by the manager and a new quote has to be created." Tom was not sure whether he was heading in the right direction.

"How would you model that?" Charles continued the question-and-answer game.

"It's definitely a loop," Tom concluded, "so either a combination of XOR gateways or a loop subprocess enclosing the create quote task and the approve task."

Charles nodded and looked at the group.

"For every customer contacted in the beginning, will the deal be closed in the end? Of course not, we all know that! And the model is still fine, as we have said that we abstract away certain details. But how often does it happen that we cannot close a deal with a customer we initially contacted? 5%? Maybe 10%?"

"Rather. 97%," somebody from the back kicked in. "At least in our company. When we try to sell a new insurance product we have a huge pile of phone numbers we call and if we are lucky then 3% of the people called will actually sign a deal."

"So is it still the default case that we come to the end of the process for each customer? Obviously not!" Charles looked around. "But the model is still fine!"

"How can the model still be fine if it reflects less than 3% of the cases?" Linda was back on board. She looked a bit puzzled.

Charles answered with a calm voice, "What we modeled here was what I call the 'happy flow.' It reflects the desirable case. The case we all wish for. We wish for closing the deal with a customer. Unfortunately, the desirable case often does not occur. There are deviations from this happy flow. Events that throw us off track. The customer jumps off. He loses interest in the offer. Negotiations about the conditions of a deal fail. Or the prospect simply chooses the product of a competitor."

Charles paused to take a deep breath. "Exceptions. These exceptions throw us off the happy flow." Again he paused. "Do we need to reflect them in the model? Any idea?"

The smart lady with the IT background entered the discussion, "I think it is worth listing what exceptions can occur at what point of the process. And probably even more important, for some exceptions it must be possible to specify reactions."

"Do you have an example?" Charles asked her.

"Maybe a lost customer could be contacted again after six months. Or at least we want to learn what went wrong. Lessons learned, so to say, as preparation for future activities. And it definitely makes a difference whether we lose a customer in the early phases as opposed to later in the process when we have already invested a lot in the customer. It is a huge difference if the customer did not show any interest right from the beginning as opposed to jumping off after the conditions have already been negotiated."

"Good points!" Charles was happy with the course of the discussion. Now it was time for him to contribute. "As a refinement of a model that only contains the happy flow, we need to specify the reactions to the unhappy events, the exceptions. And I wouldn't have brought up this topic if BPMN did not have a cure. BPMN offers nice capabilities to model such exceptions and reactions to them."

Charles walked to his desk where he had left all his teaching materials. He chose a green pen and returned to the flipchart.

"Yesterday I told you already how events can be factored into BPMN diagrams. They can be used as start events, for defining what triggers the creation of a new process instance, and as intermediate events, for defining points in a process where a certain event needs to occur in order to proceed. To be more precise, we use so called 'catching events' in BPMN to capture this case."

Charles added an intermediate event to the border of the "negotiate conditions" task. It contained a symbol that Tom had already discovered in the shape of a repository of his modeling tool, but he did not know its meaning.

"This is an attached intermediate error event."

Charles paused and looked at his students. Everyone was staring at the drawing.

"Attached intermediate error events allow you to specify the reactions to an exceptional situation. What could go wrong in 'Negotiate conditions' and what would be a possible reaction?" Charles pointed at the task in his drawing.

"Let's start a step earlier." The smart lady started lecturing. "Let's assume we have a large collection of contact data for potential customers in the first place. This is the typical situation in my company. Then most prospects are lost in the first phase, when the call center agent contacts the customer. All the prospects lost here do not need to be considered further. Therefore, a 'customer lost' exception would simply end the process. In contrast to this, losing a prospect in the 'negotiate conditions' phase is worse. With insurance products, it is often the case that the call center agent manages to talk the customer into the product. But then, when the sales rep contacts the customer again a few days later, the customer might have simply changed her mind."

"So what reaction would be appropriate for this exception?" Charles had already added a sequence flow to the intermediate error event, targeting an empty task. Now, he was ready to add a label to this task.

"Well, we know that the customer is somehow generally interested. Therefore, we should contact him or her again after a while, or come back with slightly improved conditions once the product has evolved."

Charles added "Contact again" on the flipchart.

"I don't like the task label," the lady objected. "Couldn't you put 'remember as prospect'? That's our internal wording for customers that are worth contacting again. We have a database for prospects receiving special attention when being contacted again by a call center agent."

Charles changed the label willingly and also added an intermediate error event to "Contact customer," directly leading to an end event.

"That's a good lesson to learn, by the way." Charles had turned back to the group. "Always use the vocabulary of your company! It can eliminate a lot of misunderstanding when using 'prospect' instead of 'lost customer' or 'potential customer'."

Students nodded their heads. Then the lady continued: "To finish this diagram off – the worst situation is losing a customer in the 'Close deal' phase. Here, we have already put a lot of effort into the acquisition. Even the sales manager was already involved."

Suddenly, Linda was back, "I can't imagine that a customer jumps off at this point. I mean the conditions were already negotiated, right?"

"We live in the age of the Internet," the smart lady replied. "Customers take advantage of the detailed consulting we do for our products. Then they take the conditions and search the Internet for cheaper offers. There are many Web sites out there providing detailed comparisons."

Charles enjoyed the discussion and had already attached an intermediate error event to "Close deal."

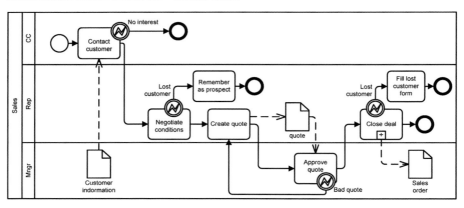

"As a reaction to this exception, the sales representative has to fill in a lost customer form," the lady explained. "If possible, we need to find out what competitor made the deal and what made the customer switch to that competitor. This is valuable input for our department that designs our insurance products."

Charles added an activity "Fill lost customer form." He smiled when the lady acknowledged that with a nod.

"Now we also covered those situations where the customer is lost. Let me just add the exception Tom mentioned earlier. Let's assume that the quote has to be adjusted in case the sales manager is not happy with it. Therefore, I attach another intermediate error event to 'approve quote'."

Charles added a sequence flow connecting this new intermediate event and "Create quote."

"I don't see why these exceptions are any different from the XOR split gateways you showed us yesterday." Linda was trying to get back into the discussion. "I mean, all we do with these attached intermediate events is to route the sequence flow in a different direction. Why do we need a separate construct?"

"Excellent observation!" Charles grinned broadly. "Indeed, we reroute the sequence flow with attached intermediate events, and we can also define different directions for the sequence flow using XOR gateways. There is a difference though! In addition to creating additional exit points for activities, attached events are of an aborting or interrupting nature. As soon as the exception is detected, the running activity is aborted and the sequence flow is rerouted."

Charles paused to make sure everybody is following him.

Linda spoke up. "What exactly do you mean by 'aborting'?"

"Let's have a look at the 'close deal' activity," Charles commenced. "In fact, it is more than a simple task. It consists of sending the quote to the customer, waiting for a response, maybe answering further questions from the customer, reminding the customer that she hasn't answered, and so on and so on."

"It is rather a collapsed subprocess, right?" somebody threw in.

"Right!" Charles responded and added the corresponding marker to his drawing, "and this model represents that as soon as it becomes obvious that the customer is lost, the remaining tasks are simply aborted."

Tom felt uncomfortable. He has not joined the discussion so far and now he was a little bit lost.

"Could we detail this subprocess?" Tom asked. "I can't really follow. I am not too much into sales processes, you know."

"Okay, no problem," Charles knew he was too fast. He flipped to a blank page on the flipchart and started all over.

"I will only include a few activities to make the point clear. Let's imagine the first task is to send the quote to the customer. Then what we expect is to receive the signed contract from the customer. In this case, we would create the sales order, and the 'close deal' subprocess would be completed. However, two other things can happen instead of receiving the signed contract." Charles took a deep breath. "Either the customer replies that he is not interested in the product any longer, or he doesn't respond at all. As we do not want to wait forever for an answer, the sales rep contacts the customer after one week. Here, again, it could turn out that the customer is actually not interested any longer."

"'Rejection' means that the customer tells us she is not interested any more?" Tom asked.

"Yes."

"And in both cases we run into a 'lost customer' exception, right?" Tom did not know about the end event with the error symbol before, but he guessed its meaning now.

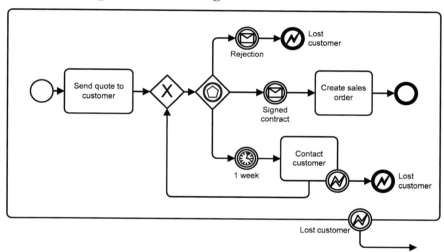

"You are absolutely right, Tom." Charles pointed at the new end events, "These constructs are called error end events. They basically terminate the current subprocess and raise the exception indicated by the label. In this case, a 'lost customer' exception is raised. The subprocess is aborted, and the sequence flow continues at the intermediate event that is attached to the subprocess."

Charles pointed to the error end event and then to the attached intermediate error event. Back to the end event and then to the intermediate event again. He repeated this a couple of times so that everybody saw the connection between these two.

"Do you remember that we made a distinction between catching and throwing events? Who can recall it?"

A guy raised his hand and started answering, "Start events are always of catching nature. Whenever a corresponding event occurs, a new process instance is created. Catching intermediate events block the sequence flow until the event occurs. In contrast to this, throwing events do not block the sequence flow in any way but, rather, a corresponding event is produced, and the process can continue immediately. End events are always throwing events. They produce an event upon completion of a process."

"Exactly! Very good!" Charles took over. "And how about attached intermediate events? What is their relationship to this catching versus throwing discussion?"

"Well," the guy continued, "I guess that only catching intermediate events can be attached to tasks and subprocesses. However, this time they do not really block the sequence flow. They are rather 'passively waiting'. I mean as long as the activity that the event is attached to is running, an event might be caught. And once the event occurs, the activity is aborted and the sequence flow is rerouted."

"This is absolutely correct!" Charles was happy about the group. "You absolutely got the point! You precisely captured the semantics!" He started laughing. "You could take over my course, I guess."

All students turned their heads to the guy that had been inconspicuous so far. For a brief moment he blushed.

After a short pause Charles continued, "So far, I have only shown you error events being attached to an activity. But other event types you already know can be used as well."

154

Charles took a deep breath. "The second most common interme-diate event to be attached is probably the timer event. Remember, the event with the clock icon inside."

Tom already felt like having a break. Yesterday, he did not really need to pay attention, as he already knew most of the stuff. Today was different. Aborting activities and rerouting sequence flow appeared to be useful concepts. However, he needed to really concentrate to get all the subtleties of the semantics.

Meanwhile, Charles went on, "Who can imagine a situation in our sales process where a timeout can abort a task or a subprocess? Or maybe an incoming message?"

Tom tried to imagine such a situation, but he simply lacked ex-perience with sales processes. Maybe, the whole process is aborted if there is still no result after a month? Probably not, he thought to him-self, one would definitely go after every sales opportunity.

"An incoming change request message!" A woman from the last row suddenly shouted out. "The customer could change his mind halfway through the process and demand another product or some slight modification. Maybe even an additional product."

"Good point!" Charles jumped to the flipchart and started draw-ing on a new page. "Let's assume that after the conditions have al-ready been negotiated, the customer can send a change request at any time to request a modified deal. Let me just quickly copy the most important activities from our previous model."

Charles flipped the pages back and forth to copy the labels of the different activities.

"This time, I omit the lanes and the data objects for simplicity."

He added the activities "contact customer," "negotiate conditions," "create quote," "approve quote," and "close deal." Before adding the sequence flow, he introduced a subprocess containing the last three activities.

"These three activities in the subprocess," Charles started explaining. "I can easily attach intermediate events to the whole region by attaching an intermediate message event to this subprocess. I represent how a change request message from the customer can arrive while I am in any of the three activities. And upon receipt of this message, the activities are aborted and the sequence flow is rerouted. In our case, we have to turn back to the 'negotiate conditions' activity."

The students looked at the new model. This was very easy, Tom thought.

He then remarked, "Charles, you also mentioned integrating timeouts into this scenario. It just came to my mind that the approval step could be a real bottleneck in this process. Imagine that a manager is not available for a certain period of time. We would not be able to wait forever for an approval. Therefore, we might introduce a timeout for the approval step. If the manager does not give his approval within three working days, this step might simply be skipped."

Charles nodded. He took his pen and added an intermediate timer event to "approve quote." He then connected the event with the "close deal" activity.

"Good idea. These are nice examples for attaching timer and message events to activities," he said. "A last thing I would like to add to this diagram is the 'lost customer' exception. Let's imagine it can occur at some time during the execution of the three activities. We can attach it to the subprocess as well."

Linda expressed her concerns, "But now we have two intermediate events attached to the same subprocess. Is this allowed?"

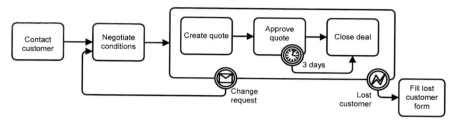

"That is exactly the point I wanted to get across," Charles said with a calm voice: "You can have as many attached events for the same activity as you like. They represent the different exit points for the events that could interrupt the execution of that activity. Change request comes in? Go this way. Lost customer exception occurs? Go that way."

Charles took a look at his gold watch. The agenda indicated that it was time for a coffee break in 15 minutes.

"I think we have already come quite far with exceptions and attached intermediate events. I suggest that we take a short break. Any objections?"

As nobody objected, Charles concluded, "After the break we will dive into transactions in BPMN. So let's get some coffee!"

The students started leaving the classroom. Tom was exhausted. What a start to the day. He was about to stand up when he recognized that Linda was still sitting at her desk. She had three differently colored highlighters in hand and went over the notes that she has taken throughout the class. The white sheet of paper showed blue, green, and pink stripes.

"I always do that," she said to Tom who was staring at her. "Colors are easier to remember."

What a geek, he thought. But how was he going to remember all this new stuff? He reached for his small notebook. He sat down next to Linda and opened a blank page.

Linda glanced over as he started writing and gave him a smile.

Attached Intermediate Error Event

Represents the exit point for the case that an exception occurs during the execution of the activity. The activity is aborted and the sequence flow is rerouted. Intermediate error events allow you to specify reactions to exceptions that happen inside the activity.

Error End Event

When reaching an error end event, an exception is thrown and the enclosing subprocess is aborted. A corresponding intermediate error event specifies the reaction to this exception.

Attached Intermediate Timer Event

Represents timeouts for activities. As soon as the time-out occurs, the activity is aborted and the sequence flow is rerouted. The timer is armed as soon as the activity starts.

Attached Intermediate Message Event

During activity execution, incoming messages lead to abortion of the activity and rerouting of the sequence flow.

Chapter 10

It's All or Nothing

"I hope the coffee brought you all up to speed," said Charles, welcoming the students back to the class, "because now we address one of the most sophisticated aspects of BPMN, transactions! You need to be focused, otherwise I'll lose you."

Tom remembered his conversation with Charles from last night. He also remembered that at some point he got lost, so he was now keen to learn what transactions have to do with business processes.

"I'll start with an academic example: Assume on Monday morning you receive a request to provide 500 chairs for a garden party in Leisure City," Charles started. "Great, you think, I can do the job. So you say 'no problem' and confirm the order. So far so good." Charles paused and looked at the group. "The bad part about it is that you neither have the chairs nor the transportation. 'No problem,' you think; I know several companies that have chairs for rent, and transportation should also be fine. Okay, what's your process ladies and gentlemen?"

"Easy!" Linda answered. "I get the chairs, get transportation, then I deliver the chairs, and get my money, all in a sequence."

"Okay, that's a good start." Charles grabbed the ball. "Assume you reserved the chairs for Friday night. Now you have to organize the transportation. You call transportation services. Sorry, no capacity on Friday. Too bad, I call the next provider to carry out my business process activity 'get transportation', you think. Bad luck. You learn that there is a big fair in town, so there is no way you can transport the chairs and fulfill your contract. What happens now?"

"You have two problems," somebody from the last row kicked in. "You need to pay for the chairs, and your customer is unhappy because he does not get what you promised. Only the chair rental service gets a deal."

Tom added, "Maybe the process was wrong? We should make the contract for the chairs *after* we have secured the transportation ..."

"... and secure the transportation only after reserving the chairs, eh?" said cheeky Linda. "It's not a problem of order."

"Good point Linda," Charles said, and Linda was all smiles. "The problem won't go away by rearranging the activities. We cannot ensure that the two things always happen together. But what can we do?" He paused for a moment, but since nobody stepped in, he continued himself, "I am sure everybody experienced such a situation before. When you book a flight but your travel plans change, what happens?"

"I cancel the flight!" Somebody threw in.

"Okay," Charles continued. "When you cancel a flight, what you actually do is to perform an activity that somehow undoes the booking of the flight. This activity compensates the booking; it is a compensating activity. And this concept exists in BPMN as well."

Tom was back to business, "So we define compensating activities for the rental of chairs. And if I later find that I do not get the trucks, I simply compensate."

"Sounds good," Charles said. "It may only require that the 500 guests of your customer will need to stand on Friday night," Charles teased Tom.

But Tom was quick, "Yes, the confirmation. The problem still remains. How about sending it once we have reserved the chairs and the truck? Then we can make sure that we only confirm customer orders if we can actually deliver."

"Interesting idea," Charles responded. "That would definitely be a valid option. But remember: competition is fierce. If you can't confirm within a certain timeframe, then your competitors will do it and you lose the deal."

"Well," Linda took the initiative, "then we have to confirm the order right away and hope that we can deliver in the end. If something goes wrong, we need to compensate the confirmation for the customer by sending a cancellation notice. The customer won't be too happy. But, still, better than losing him in the first place."

Charles was happy with the answer and said, "Time to get it modeled!" He had already grabbed a pen and started drawing rectangles on the flipchart.

"The first new BPMN construct you have to know is a transaction." Charles pointed at the big rectangle with double lines as its border. "Inside a transaction, it's all or nothing. Transactions are not specific to BPMN. They originate from the database area and have been adopted for various settings. The meaning is always the same: All things done in a transaction are either completed successfully, or they have never happened. For example, either we want to have both, the chairs and the transportation, or neither of the two."

Charles added tasks to the drawing. He halted for a second and said, "It might not be the optimal process, but let's assume that we order the chairs first and then look for transportation. Alternatively, we could do transportation first or do both in parallel." Charles kept on drawing. "If we don't find chairs, we cancel the transaction. If we don't find transportation, we cancel the transaction as well. What else do we have to do now? If we cancel the transaction, what needs to be compensated?"

"We have to inform the customer," Linda threw in. She seemed to be very excited about all this.

"Yes, Linda. We have to undo the order confirmation." Charles drew quickly and continued asking, "What has to be compensated inside the transaction?"

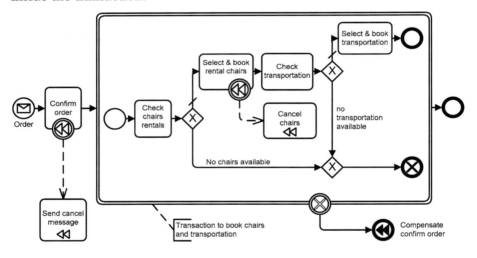

"I thought it's all or nothing," Linda replied, and her face expressed worries.

"Yes, that is the goal," Charles responded, "but if you do something that affects others, you have to take compensating actions to let them know that you want it undone."

"The availability checks do not have to be compensated," Tom stepped in. "I guess it's okay if we simply do not respond after asking for an offer. But the chair booking has to be undone."

"Yes, that's absolutely correct," Charles replied. He completed the drawing and turned back to the students, "What happens here? Your call!" He pointed at Linda.

"Well," Linda replied, "the end event with a cross and the corresponding attached event at the border of the transaction – this looks like the error handling we talked about already. I assume it is somehow the same. Or is it different?"

"You're on track, Linda. It behaves the same. It aborts the transaction and reroutes the sequence flow. The difference is that a transaction after cancellation automatically starts all compensation activities inside."

"Ah, and the compensation of the order confirmation is started explicitly," Tom threw into the discussion. "That's what the 'compensate confirm order' event says?"

"Right. It names the activity to be compensated. What has to be done is described in the compensating activities," Charles explained and pointed to 'send cancel message' and 'cancel chairs.' "Compensating activities are marked with a rewind symbol. The BPMN symbol for compensation."

Another student raised his voice, "But why is it not connected with a normal sequence flow? What does the dotted line indicate?"

"You mean the association between the attached compensation events and the compensating activity" Charles clarified. "Indeed, it is no normal sequence flow dependency. It only visualizes what should be done if compensation for an activity is started. Have a look at the catching intermediate compensation events that are attached to the activities. They don't act like the other events either. They don't even have a name. They are a way to depict that compensation might be done, and they have a directed association to indicate what should be done for compensation."

"And what happens," Linda threw in, "if the activity was not executed? Is it compensated anyway?"

"No," Charles responded, "you can only compensate activities that have been completed successfully."

"I see, because it only makes sense to cancel the chairs if I have done the booking beforehand!" Linda thought aloud.

"Correct," Charles concluded. "That's why the transportation booking does not have a compensating activity. Either it has never happened or the process is processed correctly and there is no need to compensate. Anymore questions about transactions?"

Charles grinned to the group, knowing that there must be more questions. The room was quiet. Finally, somebody raised his hand, "Can you explain this again, all this compensation and what it is good for? Does it only work in processes with transactions? How is this different from normal modeling where I have some activities to clean up before I finish the process?"

"Good point. Compensation is about cleaning up. You do not have to do it using transactions. You can use it in any process. Once you reach a point where you have 'clean up' in the sense of undoing activities you can trigger their compensation. It's a matter of style. Instead of modeling it in the normal flow, you have explicit activities, located at the tasks. You can trigger them by using the throwing intermediate compensation event, as we did here." Charles pointed at the event with the name 'Compensate confirm order' in the drawing "Or you can do it with the end event. In the sample," he kept pointing at the drawing, "it says: Okay! I'm finished at this point. But I trigger the compensation of something before I leave. I'd like cleaning up before I go."

"So, it's another style," the guy insisted. "I could also express this using normal activities that clean up before my process is done."

"Yes, modeling is a lot about style," Charles answered diplomatically and showed a bright smile that uncovered his shiny teeth.

"But what do I need the transactions for then?" The guy was not giving up. "If I can compensate explicitly, what do I need transactions for?"

"Transactions are used to express 'it's all or nothing'. It could be that the tasks inside the transactions are changes within one database transaction. Then, you do not have to have a compensating activity. The database would be informed of the cancelled transaction and undo all changes automatically. But in the business context you usually inform other people. If you cancel the transaction you need explicit activities to let them know."

Charles paused and took a long look around the class. Everybody was exhausted. Charles smiled, satisfied. He called for a fifteen-minute break. After that they would start the last part of the class.

After the break, Charles summarized all the elements of BPMN. He then encouraged everybody to model processes from his or her own work environment. Tom chose to dive deeper into the interactions with customers at LaserTec. He quickly ran into some questions he couldn't answer without asking Anne. Charles encouraged him to make assumptions and keep on modeling, but it didn't feel right. Eventually Charles asked students from the class to share their processes with the others for discussions. It wasn't necessary for Tom to present his process because Linda was eager to tell.

"Okay, Linda. Come here and explain to us what you modeled and why." Charles sat in the chair of one of the students and turned over the class to Linda. Linda stepped in front of the class, put her process model on the projector, and started explaining.

"I chose one of our latest process improvements at Mobtel. We just implemented it, that's why I could remember it the best. This process is fully automated, allowing us to handle high volumes of new customer registrations with the least effort. The process is implemented using our new process engine. It uses the functionality from other systems."

Then she started explaining the process model, "I don't want to show what the customer is doing internally. So I depicted him as a collapsed pool." She looked at Charles for confirmation, and Charles nodded.

"So, first the customer fills in the registration form. That triggers the process. I denoted it with a message start symbol here because it seemed most suitable. In our system, the process is indeed triggered by a message that is generated by the registration form when the customer submits it. The information from the form is automatically passed into our systems."

Everybody was with Linda. This Mobtel process promises to be interesting, and Linda had considerable insight on the technical level.

"The first step we take is to verify the customer registration information. The registration form already checks for completeness, but the capability is limited. That's why we include additional checks here. We want to detect spam inserted into our system and people who do not fulfill the requirements for a contract with us; for example, if they are too young. So, if that's the case, we give feedback to the customer about why we could not process the registration."

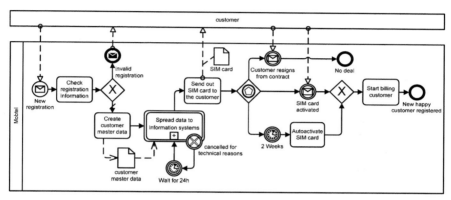

"The way you modeled it," a question from the class interrupted Linda's monologue, "as a customer, I cannot correct the information and proceed with the registration using the same process instance. You always end the process. Is that what you meant?"

"Yes, that's true. That's what we do. Customers usually start a new process anyway. Sometimes with the same invalid information. If we keep the process instance alive at this point we might end up with a bunch of pending instances in our system. That would give a wrong impression of what is going on and how many registrations are in progress. Also, I heard that the process engine has problems with too many pending instances," she explained. Linda was the king of the topic.

"But in most cases the customer information is correct. So we can go on and create the 'master data' for the customer or prospect. This step mostly involves transforming the data from the registration form into our master data format but also assigning a customer ID. Having done this, we start to put this information into our various information systems. That is stuff like the customer relationship management suite, the billing system, and other existing systems. This is an important step. We have the policy that there should never be inconsistent data in the systems. So, this is realized as a transaction. If one of the information systems is down, for example because there is an upgrade."

"Or just another software bug," somebody from the audience spoke up. The group giggled.

"So, in case any system has any problem," Linda continued with her voice raised, "we roll back the other operations to keep a consistent state. This is important, because we have other processes that rely on consistent data in all information systems. This is because.... "

"I think we all understand that," Charles interrupted. "Just continue to describe what you have modeled." Tom actually did not fully understand why this is of such importance, but he remembered the discussion about last name changes the other night.

"Yes, so if the transaction is cancelled, we pause the process for twenty-four hours and retry it. If that is all done, we can send the SIM card to the customer. Those tiny chips that you put in your mobile phone. You know?"

Everybody knew, so nobody bothered to reply to the question.

"And then there might be three things that can happen. Here, we depend on what the customer is doing. If I understood it correctly, the event-based exclusive gateway has to be used here, right?"

She looked at Charles, and he responded, "That's absolutely the correct way of using the event-based gateway. It's a race. The first event to occur determines how the process continues."

Linda was all smiles, enjoying Charles' words and feeling way ahead of the crowd.

"So in some cases the customer might withdraw from the contract. This might happen because he changed his mind. However, when the customer withdraws, there is no deal and the process ends."

"Shouldn't you delete the customer data from your systems?" Tom asked, and pointed at the transaction that Linda emphasized before.

"Um," Linda started stuttering, "I'm not sure. I mean, sure, we should.... I'm not sure if we do...." A very quiet moment passed. Linda stared into the classroom. The students stared back. "Oh,...I don't think we do." She blushed, got nervous, walked to her table, and noted down things in her calendar. She looked absentminded and worried. There was no way she could go on and finish the description of her model.

Charles got up from his seat. "Here we see how process modeling can help to find problems and how important it is to communicate processes to others in order to get feedback."

That was little help for Linda, Tom thought, and he felt sorry for her. She had to go back to work the next day and rework the newly implemented process.

"But the good thing about process models is that they communicate knowledge. So everybody should be able to interpret the models the same way. Would anybody mind explaining the rest of the Mobtel registration process?"

Nobody volunteered. Tom felt obliged to do this one. He raised his hand.

"Yes, Tom. Very good. So what happens if the customer does not withdraw?"

"Okay, he might activate the SIM card," Tom started. "In this case Mobtel can start billing the customer. The process ends with a happy new customer registered to Mobtel. When no message arrives from the customer within two weeks, the timer event occurs. That means the process proceeds this way and the customer SIM card is auto activated. This process branch merges with the other one, so here they also start billing the customer and treat that as just another happy customer. By the way, why would you do that?"

Tom turned toward Linda.

"Well," she started, "we cannot let the process get stuck there forever. So we trigger it forward and bill the customer. If the customer is unhappy with that we have other processes to handle that."

Some in the class nodded knowingly. Everyone was happy with the answer, and Charles took time to discuss Linda's model.

The lesson went on with two other students explaining their processes. Tom's attention was fading away. The two days of training added a lot to his BPMN understanding. Would he be able to gain from it? He pulled out his notebook and reviewed the notes he had taken since he started working for LaserTec. When he flipped to the first empty page he recalled the new BPMN elements added in this last session. He started noting them down. He knew that he was well equipped now, but how would all this go into his daily work at LaserTec? He would need to talk about this with Anne and Haffner.

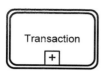

Transaction

A transaction is a set of activities that logically belong together. Transactions have all-or-nothing semantics.

Intermediate Cancel Event

Can be attached to transactions only. They show what should happen in case a transaction is cancelled.

Cancel End Event

Can be used within a transaction. It explicitly triggers the cancellation of the transaction.

Compensation Activity

Specifies what needs to be done to compensate a completed activity. Compensation is typically triggered through the cancellation of an enclosing transaction.

Intermediate Catching Compensation Event

Is always attached to an activity. It relates this activity to its compensation activity using a directed association from the event to the compensation activity.

Intermediate Throwing Compensation Event

Allows to explicitly trigger the compensation of individual activities within the normal sequence flow of the process.

Compensation End Event
Has the same purpose as the intermediate throwing compensation event and is used if nothing needs to be done afterwards.

Chapter 11

What's Next?

"Hello, Tom! " Anne exclaimed when she saw him standing in the door. "How was your training?"

Tom was more than happy to talk about his trip; about the hotel, the setting, about Linda and all the other class mates with their different backgrounds. Tom showed some of the samples that they drew in class and kept talking. Anne listened carefully. She would have loved to go to this training herself. But now she used Tom to bring her up to date with BPMN concepts. Tom realized that he has become a teacher to Anne instead of being her student. He enjoyed his new role.

"Okay, exceptions are another possibility to alter the sequence flow, right?" Anne concluded after a longer discussion.

"It's more. When throwing an exception, you abort every activity inside the subprocess. And from there on, it's escalated upwards until the exception is caught and handled. It's a matter of philosophy. You can alter the sequence flow based on data, but if you need to reflect that an undesired situation needs extra effort to be dealt with, then you should use exceptions," Tom explained.

"How was Charles, by the way?" Anne instantly changed the topic. Her eyes glowed as if Charles were a rock star.

"Nice guy," Tom answered. The social event and the long night in the bar crossed his mind. "He has a lot of anecdotes to tell."

Tom continued telling stories from the workshop. Anne was following every word. They emptied two cups of coffee each before they even thought about it. Tom remembered his very first day at LaserTec when he was not used to Anne's coffee and she was the one telling about BPMN. A lot had changed in the last few months. Now he was the process expert at LaserTec, and that felt good. He was capable of modeling everything.

"Welcome back, Mr. Bauer." Haffner's voice filled the room, and Tom and Anne turned to him. They were so much into their discussion that they did not hear him enter the room. "I hope the training was successful and brought new insights for LaserTec!"

"Oh yes, the training was great. We learned about all these advanced modeling constructs, including exceptions and business transactions." Tom couldn't wait to explain it all to Haffner.

"That is all very nice, Mr. Bauer, but actually I was hoping for more strategic findings."

Tom felt uncomfortable, not knowing exactly what Haffner was up to.

"See, the question for me is, what do I do with all these nice processes? To be frank, I don't care for transactions and exceptions, I care for business value. What are the new options for LaserTec? This is what I need to know," Haffner said in a serious but not unfriendly tone.

"Actually, we have briefly touched on these options before, regarding the business process management lifecycle," Anne stepped in. "It consists of the phases in which process management initiatives can be organized."

"Process lifecycle?" Haffner asked.

"The BPM lifecycle, of course," Anne stepped in. "It represents the idea to iteratively analyze and improve business processes. The first phase is the design of processes."

"And the result of the design phase is the process model," Haffner concluded.

"Not quite," Anne responded. She took a sheet of paper and started drawing. "The process model is the central artifact that helps to communicate the real processes throughout all the phases. An initial analysis creates the first As-Is process models. They represent the current situation. In the process design phase, you already create the ideal new process. The To-Be situation."

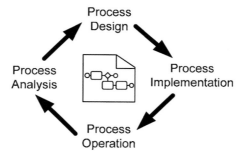

Haffner and Tom leaned over to see Anne's drawing. Anne kept explaining, "and if you want this newly designed process to become reality you need to implement it."

"I see, I see," Haffner interrupted. "By 'implementation,' you mean change management, right?"

"Exactly," Anne responded. "It's about implementing the new

processes in the organization."

Haffner nodded and said, "That's essential. You have to get everybody on board. If you fail to convince your staff about the advantages of the new procedures they will go back to the old ones." Anne smiled at Haffner knowingly.

"From the conversations at the workshop," Tom said, "I had another association. Many people talked about software projects for process implementation."

"Sure," Anne responded. "Depending on your environment, software projects for automated processes will be needed. It's all about bringing the desired processes to life. Some manual activities can be sped up by having appropriate software systems at hand; other activities might be automated altogether. Especially if you do a lot of information processing, modern computer systems can take over a lot of activities that were previously done manually."

"And also reduce manual hand-overs," Tom remarked.

"Exactly," Anne said. "Remember the order dispatching I showed you in the very beginning?"

"Sure," Tom replied.

Anne continued, "If you introduced a Web-based interface for your customers you could save a lot of the data entry stuff I do every day. And even better, the data could already be checked for consistency before the customer submits it. That might also save a lot of time."

Haffner didn't listen to the discussion. He was still staring at Anne's drawing of the lifecycle.

"And this is operations," Haffner finally said, pointing at the drawing. "That's what we do all day. That's what we always did, only now we call it process operation."

"Well," Anne responded, "it also means looking at the daily work from the process perspective. It's not only about the individual workload. People need to have a shared understanding of the dependencies. That helps them to adjust the daily routines to enable a better process flow."

"And then we run in the cycle. We analyze the process in operation." Tom tried to get the ball game.

"We need KPIs there. That will tell us where to optimize the process," Haffner burst out.

Tom knew from his university days that KPIs are "key performance indicators" and a management instrument to boil down business goals to numbers. But he had not yet thought about them in the context of business processes.

"Yes," Anne took over again. "That is indeed how you can manage this. You need a goal value, like five weeks from order to installation, then you can streamline the process to achieve that goal. KPIs are well suited to be associated with processes."

Haffner kicked in, "With the process models at hand, we can position the KPIs and directly pinpoint where we need to get better."

"But how can we collect the data to measure these KPIs? This sounds like a big overhead," Tom asked.

Haffner turned to Anne, waiting for an answer. After a short pause she replied, "Ideally, we could extract a lot of information from the software systems we use. Tom, you mentioned process implementation in software systems. If you have a certain degree of process automation at hand, you typically get the numbers for free. If not, it might involve some effort to collect them."

"Just think of the possibilities!" Haffner smiled. "Running through this process cycle over and over helps us sharpen our processes and improve the company. Remember, Mr. Bauer, when we first talked during your job interview? I wanted you to get a deep understanding of what is going on at LaserTec."

Tom nodded.

Haffner went on, "Now I really see the framework to achieve that. With the process models at hand we finally have a language to communicate about what we do on a day-to-day basis. It puts it into perspective and explains its connection to the overall value creation at LaserTec. With the lifecycle, we really have a way to leverage the new understanding we gain. And the process models are the central artifacts to communicate that."

Haffner suddenly stopped talking. Anne and Tom stared at him, waiting for him to continue.

"When I started this, I wanted to understand what we do. But now I see how I can use the process perspective to *steer* what we are doing. We can think about process improvement and process automation in a much more structured way."

Haffner stopped again. He looked at Tom and asked, "Are you ready, Mr. Bauer?"

Tom raised an eyebrow. He was not quite sure what Haffner meant. "The process documentation work you did, Mr. Bauer, was an important first step. But now I want you to step up to lead LaserTec's efforts in process improvement and automation. You run the cycle. Don't think the story ends here, Mr. Bauer, it just started! "

Recommended Reading and Resources

Visit the Web site for this book:
www.bpmn-book.com

The Web site for this book provides more information about BPMN: News and upcoming versions of the BPMN standard; links to BPMN tutorials; links to BPMN related blogs and communities; additional books on BPMN and BPM in general; and Errata (let us know about issues in the current version of the book). Here's a *small* sampling of the Web resources you'll find at the site:

Object Management Group:
- Business Process Management Initiative
- BPMN Information Home

Bruce Silver's *BPMS Watch* blog and series, "BPMN and the Business Process Expert."

BPTrends.com: a primary source of news and information relating to all aspects of business process change, focused on trends, directions and best practices.

Ismael Ghalimi's *BPM 2.0*: a blog by a BPMI.org co-founder.

Sandy Kemsley's *Column 2.0*: an independent analyst's blog on BPM.

David Frankel's *MDA Journal*.

Vishal Saxena's blog: *Things BPMN - Vishal's BPM corner*.

Other Books on BPMN

White, Stephen and Derek Miers, *BPMN Modeling and Reference Guide, Future Strategies Inc.*, 2008. Experts Stephen White (IBM) and Derek Miers (BPMFocus) have been involved in the development of the BPMN standard since the early days of BPMI.org. As Work Group chair and Specification Editor since its inception, Dr. White was instrumental in creating the BPMN standard and is now guiding its continuing refinement at the OMG. Derek Miers has played a leading role in the BPMN space, first as Co-Chair of BPMI.org and more recently within the OMG.

Silver, Bruce, *BPMN Method and Style,* 2009. Through his company BPMessentials, Silver has delivered BPMN training and certification to over 1000 students, and is a key contributor to version 2.0 of the BPMN standard in OMG. Based on BPMN 2.0, the book provides a concrete methodology and consistent modeling style, critical to BPMN's promise of a common language shared by business and IT. The method and style are described at three levels: descriptive modeling for business users (Level 1), analytical modeling for analysts and architects (Level 2), and executable modeling in BPMN (Level 3), a new capability of BPMN 2.0.

Saxena, Vishal, *Patterns with BPMN 2.0,* 2009. Saxena is a senior product development manager in the Oracle Application Server division. He currently leads the development of Business Process Analysis (BPA) and Business Process Management (BPM) Suite. He brings extensive experience in the enterprise software development, integration and BPM industry over the past 14 years. He works closely on the BPMN standards at OMG. Besides leading development teams in multiple time zones, he is out evangelizing Oracle's BPM solution with customers, partners and analysts.

About the Authors

The authors are members of the Business Process Technology research group of the Hasso Plattner Institute for IT Systems Engineering at the University of Potsdam, Germany. http://bpt.hpi.uni-potsdam.de

The group is led by Professor Mathias Weske, who has 15 years of experience in research and teaching workflow technology and business process management. He is also the author of the textbook, *Business Process Management: Concepts, Languages, Architectures.*

Alexander Grosskopf and Gero Decker, hold Masters degrees in IT Systems Engineering and are researchers in business process management, with both academic and industry experience. They work with key contributors to the BPMN standardization body, OMG, in the areas of execution semantics and choreographies.

The authors actively promote the value of business process management and professional process-based communication. The authors teach business process technology and BPMN to university students, industry professionals and administrative staff in the public sector.

Gero and Mathias are among the founders of signavio.com, a company specializing in business process modeling on the Web.

Your Complete BPM Library
Innovation at the Intersection of Business and Technology
www.mkpress.com